FESTIVALS AND SPECIAL DAYS IN BRITAIN

CONTENTS

❧ Pupils with one o...
❧❧ Pupils with two o...
❧❧❧ Pupils with three ...
◆ Festivals celebrate...
   form the multi-cul...
   and which are mor...

C000232408

A small clock at the top of each page gives the approximate duration of each activity.

PUPILS WITH ONE OR MORE YEARS OF ENGLISH

PUPILS WITH TWO OR MORE YEARS OF ENGLISH

Information about the festivals featured in this book

Back to School (Pages 12–14)
The school year in England, Wales and Northern Ireland begins in the first week of September. Children start primary school when they are four or five years old. The first class in primary school is called Reception, then pupils progress through Years 1–6. They start secondary school when they are 11 years old in Year 7. At the end of Year 11, when they are 16 years old, pupils sit the GCSE (General Certificate of Secondary Education) exams in around 8–10 subjects. Maths, English, a science and a foreign language are compulsory and pupils choose their remaining examination subjects from those offered at their school. The remaining two years at secondary school are not compulsory and are known as the Sixth Form; the first year is the Lower Sixth and the second year is the Upper Sixth. Pupils in the Sixth Form generally study for examinations which will lead to a place in university or college. Scotland has a different school year and examination system from the rest of the UK.

Harvest Festival (Pages 15–16)
Harvest Festival is a Christian festival of thanksgiving for all the good things we have. There is no set date for Harvest Festival but it usually takes place in September or sometimes October. It is traditional to take gifts of food to elderly people after the church or school Harvest Festival. At one time, these gifts were locally grown fruit and vegetables, but nowadays it is more common to offer dried and tinned foods. Many churches also hold a Harvest Supper. A traditional decoration is the 'Corn Dolly', made from straw.

Rosh Hashanah (Pages 17–18)
Rosh Hashanah is the Jewish New Year. It is celebrated on the first day of the Jewish month *Tishri*, which occurs in September according to the western calendar. It is a time to ask God's forgiveness for the wrongdoings of the past year. At the beginning of the Rosh Hashanah service a *shofar* (ram's horn) is blown to call the worshippers to prayer. Apples dipped in honey are eaten for a good and sweet new year.

Clocks Go Back (Pages 19–20)
The clocks in the UK go back an hour at midnight on the last Saturday in October. This marks the end of British Summer Time and a return to Greenwich Mean Time. British Summer Time lasts from the end of March until the end of October. The clocks going back is not a festival; in fact most people dread the darker nights and the cold weather to come after this date.

Hallowe'en (Pages 21–24)
Hallowe'en is celebrated on 31 October. It was originally the Celtic festival of the dead, known as *Samhain*. The Christian church tried to suppress this pagan festival, renaming it All Hallows' Eve

(hence the name Hallowe'en). However, the festival remains essentially pagan and has been banned in some Christian schools in Britain. Pumpkin lanterns, masks and costumes are all part of Hallowe'en, as is the custom of 'trick or treat'. This involves children in costumes going from house to house asking for treats such as sweets, fruit and money. If the householder refuses to give them a treat, the children may then play a trick or practical joke on them.

Bonfire Night (Pages 25–29)
Bonfire Night is celebrated on 5 November. It falls on the date when, in 1605, a group of Catholics tried to blow up the Houses of Parliament in London. This was known as the Gunpowder Plot. It was a time of great religious and political unrest in England and the Catholics were suffering persecution at the hands of the Protestant government. The plan failed and the plotters were put to death. The festival is also known as Guy Fawkes' Night, after the man who laid the explosives in the cellars of the Houses of Parliament. It is still the custom to burn an effigy of Guy Fawkes, called a 'guy', on the bonfire. Bonfire Night has survived to this day, perhaps because people welcome the opportunity to have a bonfire, fireworks and a party in the cold, dark month of November.

Diwali (Pages 30–31)
Diwali is a Hindu festival which takes place on the 15th day of the month of *Kartik* according to the Hindu calendar (October or November in the western calendar). The name comes from the word *diva*, which is a small lamp. A story which is associated with Diwali is that of Rama and Sita (see page 31). Many Hindus also celebrate new year at this time. Many Hindus in Britain celebrate Diwali with fireworks in the local park. The Hindu population in Britain is currently 155,000 (1999 figures).

Christmas (Pages 34–38)
The name 'Christmas' comes from 'Christ's Mass'. It is celebrated on 25 December, when people visit their families, exchange presents and eat a Christmas dinner of turkey and Christmas pudding. Practising Christians usually attend Midnight Mass on Christmas Eve and go to church again on the morning of Christmas Day. It is the tradition for children to leave out a stocking when they go to bed on Christmas Eve for Father Christmas to fill with presents. Christmas Day and Boxing Day (26 December) are both bank holidays (public holidays) in the UK.

A Christmas Carol (Page 38)
Charles Dickens (1812–1870) is one of the most famous and enduringly popular of English novelists. Film and cartoon versions of his novel *A Christmas Carol* (see page 38) are shown nearly every year on British television. It is the story of Ebenezer Scrooge, a rich but miserly old

man. He learns to become more benevolent when he is visited on Christmas Eve by three ghosts who show him what the consequences will be if he doesn't change. Novels by Dickens include *The Pickwick Papers* (1837), *Oliver Twist* (1838), *Nicholas Nickleby* (1839), *The Old Curiosity Shop* (1841), *A Christmas Carol* (1842), *David Copperfield* (1850), *A Tale of Two Cities* (1859) and *Great Expectations* (1861).

New Year (Pages 39–41)
In Britain, New Year's Eve is celebrated on 31 December when many people hold parties or go to pubs and night clubs. Many of the New Year traditions practised in Britain come from Scotland, where the festival is know as *Hogmanay*. All over the UK, people join hands at midnight and sing the Scottish song 'Auld Lang Syne' by Robert Burns. In Scotland the New Year is welcomed by the playing of bagpipes and the custom of 'first footing' – this involves visiting friends and relatives after midnight. It is lucky if the 'first footer' is a dark-haired man bringing a gift of coal and a bottle of whisky. New Year's Day is a bank holiday in the UK.

Ramadan and Id-ul-Fitr (Pages 42–43)
Ramadan and Id-ul-Fitr fall a few days earlier every year according to the western calendar, as the Muslims have a lunar calendar. Ramadan is the ninth month of the Muslim calendar and is the month of fasting. Most Muslim people do not eat or drink between sunrise and sunset during Ramadan. This is to help them live as better Muslims. Id-ul-Fitr is the festival at the end of the month of Ramadan. On the last day of Ramadan, many people watch for the new moon, which marks the end of the fast. Id-ul-Fitr is a time for visiting friends and relatives, exchanging gifts and having a special meal. The Muslim population in the UK is currently 580,000 (1999 figures).

Chinese New Year (Pages 44–45)
There is a big Chinese New Year festival in Chinatown in London every year. The Chinese New Year is celebrated in January or February. It is the most important festival in the Chinese year. The festivities traditionally include firecrackers and dragon dances. Special foods such as dumplings and cakes are eaten. Red is a lucky colour for the new year, and children are given lucky red envelopes filled with money.

Burns Night (Pages 46–47)
Robert (or 'Robbie') Burns (1759–1796) is Scotland's national poet. He wrote many poems and songs in Scottish dialect. His birthday (25 January) is celebrated in Scotland as Burns Night. Customs include eating haggis (a traditional Scottish dish of minced meat) and drinking whisky, playing the bagpipes and reciting poems

by Burns. The Burns Night dinner is usually followed by singing and a *ceilidh* (traditional Scottish dancing).

Valentine's Day (Pages 48–50)

Valentine's Day is the festival of lovers and is celebrated on 14 February. People send an anonymous card to the person they would like to be their girlfriend or boyfriend. St Valentine was an early Christian who was put to death for his beliefs. He is said to have left a message for his beloved on the wall of his prison cell, signed 'Your Valentine'.

Pancake Day (Pages 51–53)

Pancake Day is the popular name for Shrove Tuesday, the day before Lent starts. In the days when people fasted during Lent, Shrove Tuesday was the last day they could enjoy themselves. Pancakes are the traditional dish for Shrove Tuesday, eaten with lemon juice and sugar. The name Shrove Tuesday comes from the verb 'to shrive', which means 'to make a confession', as this was the day for people to confess their sins before Lent started. Although it is unusual for Christians to fast during Lent these days, many people give up something they enjoy during this period, often sweets, chocolate or alcohol.

Patron Saints' Days (Pages 56–58)

St David is the patron saint of Wales and his feast day is 1 March. Little is known about his life, except that he was the primate of South Wales in the sixth century and founded many churches there. St David's, in South Wales, was the place of his shrine and became a place of pilgrimage. The feast day of **St Patrick**, the patron saint of Ireland, is 17 March. Born in Wales in around 389 AD, he was kidnapped by Irish marauders at the age of 16. After six years he escaped to France and spent a few years in a monastery there. On his return to Britain he was ordained as a bishop and went to Ireland as a missionary. He established churches in the north of Ireland. **St George**'s feast day is 23 April. He is the patron saint of England. A traditional story about him is that he killed a dragon to save a princess from being eaten. **St Andrew** is the patron saint of Scotland. His feast day, 30 November, falls outside the spring period covered in this section of the book. He has been included here as all the other patron saints' days occur in the spring.

Mother's Day (Pages 59–61)

In Britain, Mother's Day is celebrated on the Sunday three weeks before Easter so it usually occurs in March. Mother's Day is the popular name for Mothering Sunday, the day when Christians used to return to the 'mother church' for the Sunday service. Later, when many young girls left home to become servants and boys went to be apprentices, the festival became a holiday for young people to visit their mothers. It was the custom to take flowers and gifts. Many young girls were given a 'simnel cake' to take home to their mothers.

Comic Relief (Pages 62–64)

Comic Relief is a recent addition to the festivals calendar. It began in the 1980s to raise money for charity projects in Britain and Africa. It takes place in March every two years (the last one was in 1999). There is a big build-up to Comic Relief day (which is a Friday) on television, and people all over the country organise fund-raising events. The idea is to make fund-raising fun so all the events must be humorous. Red noses (for people and for cars, similar to those worn by clowns) are sold, giving the day the popular name of 'Red Nose Day'.

April Fool's Day (Pages 65–66)

April Fool's Day is on 1 April. People play tricks and practical jokes on their friends. If the friends fall for the joke, they are 'April Fools'. Traditionally, the tricks must be played before midday. If someone plays an April Fool's trick after midday, he or she is the fool.

Easter (Pages 67–69)

Palm Sunday is the Sunday before Easter and celebrates the arrival of Jesus in Jerusalem. Small crosses made of palm leaves are given to church-goers to mark the occasion.
Maundy Thursday is the Thursday before Easter and commemorates the Last Supper of Jesus and his disciples. It is the day when the Queen gives small purses of money to some specially chosen people. Originally the sovereign used to wash the people's feet, too, as Christ once washed the disciples' feet.
Good Friday commemorates the crucifixion of Jesus. The name comes from 'God' rather than 'good'.
Easter Sunday is the day for celebrating Jesus's rising from the dead. It falls on the first Sunday after the spring full moon, in March or April. Chocolate Easter eggs are given to children on this day.
Easter Monday, the day after Easter, is a bank holiday in the UK, as is Good Friday.

May Day (Pages 70–71)

The first day of May is traditionally the festival of the coming of spring. It is usually celebrated with Maypole dancing (see pages 70–71) and Morris dancing. In some towns a May Queen is elected. The May Queen is a beautiful girl who is crowned with a garland of flowers and then goes on a procession around the town. The first Monday in May is a bank holiday in the UK.

Sports Day (Pages 74–75)

Every school in the UK has a sports day in June or July, shortly before the summer holidays. The event usually takes up a whole day and parents come to watch. Traditional races for primary school children include the 'egg and spoon race' (running while holding an egg on a spoon), 'the three-legged race' (in which two people run with their adjacent legs

tied together) and the 'obstacle race'. Secondary school pupils compete in athletics events, such as running races, the high jump and long jump and javelin throwing.

Summer Fête (Pages 76–77)

Many schools, churches and other organisations, such as the boy scouts and girl guides, hold a fund-raising summer fête in June or July. There are stalls selling home-baked cakes, crafts and second-hand items. There are always games at the fête. Popular games include: the 'tombola', in which people pick numbered tickets to try and win a prize; 'guess the weight of the cake', in which people try to win the cake (variations include 'guess the name of the doll', 'guess how many coins in the jar', etc.); and 'hoopla' (in which people try to throw a hoop over the prizes). Food and drinks are also sold and nowadays there is often a barbecue.

Father's Day (Pages 78–79)

Father's Day is the third Sunday in June. It is a new festival, introduced to provide fathers with a similar occasion to Mother's Day. Children give their fathers cards and presents.

Summer Holidays (Pages 80–84)

Schools break up for the long summer holidays in the third week of July. Children are then on holiday until the first week of September. Naturally this is the time when many families go on their annual holiday. Most British people go away for two weeks, usually abroad. Popular holiday destinations include Spain, Greece and Portugal.

Notting Hill Carnival (Pages 85–87)

The Notting Hill Carnival is a big Caribbean festival which takes place every year in Notting Hill in London. Carnival is always on the August bank holiday weekend (the last Sunday and Monday in August). The first Carnival took place in August 1964 and was organised by some Notting Hill inhabitants from Trinidad. Since then, the Carnival has grown and now attracts nearly two million visitors every year. The Carnival procession includes dancers and music. The traditional Carnival music is played by steel bands.

Highland Games (Pages 88–89)

The Highland Games take place all over Scotland in late August and early September. The most famous event is 'tossing the caber' in which men throw a huge tree trunk as far as they can. Other events include hammer throwing, the hill race, the tug-of-war (in which two teams pull on either end of a rope to try to pull the other team over a line marked on the ground), bagpipe-playing competitions and Scottish dancing competitions. The Highland Games end with a huge pillow fight in which everyone can take part.

Festivals and Special Days

There are four seasons in the year. Do you know which months are in each season?
Write the names of the months.

AUTUMN	WINTER	SPRING	SUMMER
S _ _ _ _ _ _ _ _	D _ _ _ _ _ _ _	M _ _ _ _ _	J _ _ _
O _ _ _ _ _ _ _	J _ _ _ _ _ _ _	A _ _ _ _ _	J _ _ _
N _ _ _ _ _ _ _	F _ _ _ _ _ _ _	M _ _	A _ _ _ _ _ _

These are some British festivals. Read about the festivals.
Write the name of each festival in the correct month on the calendar.

Hallowe'en

This is the festival of ghosts, witches and vampires.
It is in the Autumn. This month has got two Os in it.

St Patrick's Day

St Patrick is the patron saint of Ireland. St Patrick's Day is in the Spring. This month has got five letters. The last letter is H.

Valentine's Day

This is the festival for people in love. It's in the Winter. This month has got eight letters. The third letter is B.

St Andrew's Day

St Andrew is the patron saint of Scotland. St Andrew's Day is in the Autumn. This month has got eight letters.

Christmas Day

This is the most important Christian festival of the year. It is in the Winter. This month has got eight letters. The fifth letter is M.

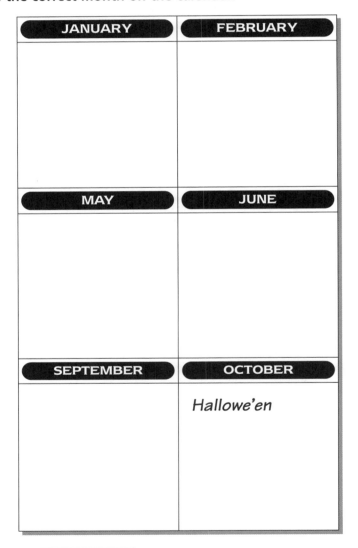

JANUARY	FEBRUARY
MAY	**JUNE**
SEPTEMBER	**OCTOBER**
	Hallowe'en

Father's Day

On Father's Day children give presents and cards to their dad. It's in the Summer. This month has got four letters. The third letter is N.

Bonfire Night

This is a festival with fireworks and bonfires. It's in the Autumn. The third letter of this month is V.

May Day

This is the Spring festival. It's in May, of course.

New Year's Day

This is the first day of the new year. It's in the Winter. The first letter of this month is J.

Mother's Day

On Mother's Day children give presents and cards to their mum. It's in the Spring. This month has got five letters. The first letter is M.

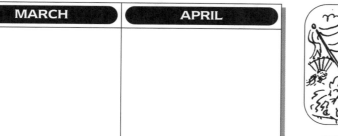

MARCH	APRIL
JULY	AUGUST
NOVEMBER	DECEMBER

Notting Hill Carnival

This is a big Caribbean carnival in London. It's in the Summer. The first letter of this month is not J.

Back to School

This is when the new school year starts. Everybody goes back to school after the summer holidays. It's in the Autumn. This month has got nine letters.

St David's Day

St David is the patron saint of Wales. St David's Day is in the Spring. This month has got five letters. The second letter is A.

April Fool's Day

On April Fool's Day people play tricks on their friends. It's in March. Only joking! It's in April, of course.

St George's Day

St George is the patron saint of England. St George's Day is in the Spring. The first letter of this month is A.

Summer Holidays

This isn't a festival but it is the end of school and the start of the summer holidays. This month is in the Summer. The first letter is J and the last letter is Y.

Birthday Parties

**British teenagers often organise a party for their birthdays.
They give invitations to all their friends.**

What are these people doing for their birthdays? Write the names on the invitations.

| Simon | Helen | Rashid | Louise |

| Matthew | Davina | Hamish | Natasha |

1
It's my birthday
on Saturday 12 July.
Please come to a picnic at 1 p.m.
Lots of love

....

2
Please come bowling
on my birthday:
Wednesday 7 February at 5 p.m.
Lots of love

....

3
Would you like to come
to the cinema on my birthday?
Please come on
Friday 28 March at 6 p.m.
Love from

....

4
It's my birthday
on Monday 15 October.
We're going to the theme park.
Please come at 1 p.m.
From

....

5
Please come to
celebrate my birthday on
Tuesday 4 December. We're going
to the restaurant at 6 p.m.
Love from

....

6
Would you like to
come skating on my birthday?
Please come on
Thursday 10 April at 7 p.m.
Love

....

7
It's my birthday
on Saturday 2 September.
Please come to the theatre
with us at 8 p.m.
From

....

8
Would you like to come
to my birthday party?
It's on Sunday 30 May at 6 p.m.
Lots of love

....

Solve the anagrams and write the words in the grid.
What is in the mystery birthday present?

cincip

wobling

mincea

methe rapk

raunstreat

tikangs

treathe

trypa

Birthday Presents

In Britain, it's usual to give presents to the birthday girl or boy.

It's Rachel's birthday. She has got lots of presents from her friends and family. However, she's not happy. She doesn't like any of her presents.

Read what she says. Which present is she talking about in each sentence?

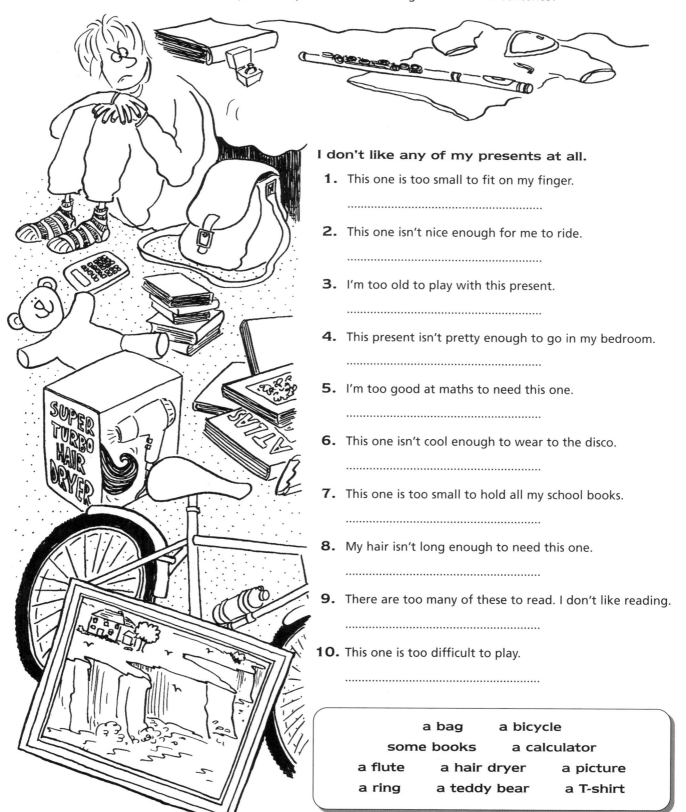

I don't like any of my presents at all.

1. This one is too small to fit on my finger.

   ....

2. This one isn't nice enough for me to ride.

   ....

3. I'm too old to play with this present.

   ....

4. This present isn't pretty enough to go in my bedroom.

   ....

5. I'm too good at maths to need this one.

   ....

6. This one isn't cool enough to wear to the disco.

   ....

7. This one is too small to hold all my school books.

   ....

8. My hair isn't long enough to need this one.

   ....

9. There are too many of these to read. I don't like reading.

   ....

10. This one is too difficult to play.

    ....

a bag   a bicycle

some books   a calculator

a flute   a hair dryer   a picture

a ring   a teddy bear   a T-shirt

What's in the Picture?

Which of these things can you see in the picture? Tick the things you can see.

1. a butterfly ☐
2. grass ☐
3. a house ☐
4. an elephant ☐
5. a dog ☐
6. a man ☐
7. the sun ☐
8. nuts ☐
9. a boy ☐
10. tomatoes ☐
11. a mouse ☐
12. a ghost ☐
13. a monkey ☐
14. a baby ☐
15. a fox ☐
16. oranges ☐
17. a girl ☐
18. mushrooms ☐
19. leaves ☐
20. birds ☐
21. a rainbow ☐
22. an umbrella ☐
23. bananas ☐
24. squirrels ☐
25. a rabbit ☐
26. spiders ☐
27. flowers ☐
28. a woman ☐
29. cherries ☐
30. trees ☐

Colour the numbers of the things in the picture. Find an autumn fruit. What is it?

Find the Differences

Find the differences between the two pictures. Write sentences about them.
Use these phrases:

> lots of/plenty of   a few   a couple of   one

For example:

In picture A there are lots of leaves on the tree.

....

In picture B there are a few leaves on the tree.

....

....

....

....

....

....

....

....

....

....

....

The Back to School Alphabet

It's the beginning of September and it's time to go back to school.
Look at all the school pictures. Write the words under the pictures.

atlas, bag, calculator, dictionary,
exercise books, football, gym, homework,
infants, jacket, kids, lunch, magazine, notebook,
overhead projector, pens and pencils, questions,
ruler, sports kit, teacher, uniform, violin, watch,
xylophone, yawn, zero

A	**B**

C	**D**	**E**	**F**
G	**H**	**I**	**J**
K	**L**	**M**	**N**
O	**P**	**Q**	**R**
S	**T**	**U**	**V**
W	**X**	**Y**	**Z**

Going Back to School

It is the first day back at school for Shona, Natalie, Daniel, Nathan, Raminder and James.

Look at the information and read what the people say.
Which year is each person in? How does each person travel to school?
What is the name of each person's teacher? Complete the table.

Year at school and ages of pupils	
Year 7:	age 11–12
Year 8:	age 12–13
Year 9:	age 13–14
Year 10:	age 14–15
Year 11:	age 15–16
Sixth form: (two years)	age 16–18

Teachers and number of pupils in the class	
Mr Raman:	18 pupils
Ms Martinez:	22 pupils
Mr Bryant:	26 pupils
Mrs Peel:	28 pupils
Mr Turton:	30 pupils
Ms Moore:	32 pupils

Transport and journey times to school	
walking:	5 minutes
van:	10 minutes
bike:	12 minutes
bus:	15 minutes
car:	16 minutes
train:	20 minutes

Shona: I am three years younger than James. There are six more pupils in my class than in Raminder's. My journey is five minutes longer than Daniel's.

Nathan: I am one year older than Raminder. There are ten more people in my class than in Natalie's. My journey is four mintues shorter than James's.

Natalie: I am five years older than Shona. There are twelve fewer pupils in my class than in James's. My journey is ten minutes longer than Shona's.

Raminder: I am three years younger than Daniel. There are four more people in my class than in Daniel's. My journey is three minutes longer than Nathan's.

Daniel: I am one year younger than Natalie. There are six fewer pupils in my class than in Nathan's. My journey is ten minutes shorter than Raminder's.

James: I am one year older than Nathan. There are two fewer people in my class than in Shona's. My journey is four minutes shorter than Natalie's.

	Year	Name of teacher	Transport
Shona	Year 7		
Natalie			
Daniel			walking
Nathan			
Raminder		Mr Bryant	
James			

1. Who is the oldest?

....

2. Who is in the biggest class?

....

3. Who has the shortest journey to school?

....

4. Who goes to school by car?

....

5. Who is in Year 9?

....

6. Who is in Mr Bryant's class?

....

GCSE Options

In England, Wales and Northern Ireland pupils start studying for their GCSE (General Certificate of Secondary Education) exams in Year 10. They can choose nine subjects. Some of the subjects are **compulsory** (you have to do them) and some are **optional** (you can choose them if you like).

These are the subjects pupils can take at Littleton Comprehensive School.

If you were starting in Year 10, which nine subjects would you choose?

You must do compulsory subjects, but you can choose your optional subjects. You can't choose subjects that clash (are at the same time).

If you chose these subjects, what would your timetable be? Complete your timetable.

Littleton Comprehensive School GCSE Options	
☐ **Maths** (compulsory)	Tuesday Session 1; Wednesday Session 3
Sciences (at least one science is compulsory)	
☐ **General Science**	Monday Session 1, Thursday Session 3
☐ **Biology**	Monday Session 2, Wednesday Session 2
☐ **Chemistry**	Thursday Sessions 3 and 4
☐ **Physics**	Monday Session 1, Tuesday Session 2
☐ **English** (compulsory)	Monday Session 4, Thursday Session 1
Modern languages (at least one langage is compulsory)	
☐ **French**	Thursday Session 2, Friday Session 3
☐ **German**	Monday Session 3, Wednesday Session 1
☐ **Spanish**	Monday Session 3, Wednesday Session 1
☐ **Italian**	Tuesday Session 2, Thursday Session 4
☐ **Russian**	Monday Session 2, Wednesday Session 2
☐ **Design and Technology** (optional)	Friday Sessions 1 and 2
☐ **Religious Studies** (optional)	Tuesday Sessions 3 and 4
☐ **History** (optional)	Tuesday Session 2, Thursday Session 4
☐ **Politics** (optional)	Monday Session 3, Wednesday Session 1
☐ **Drama** (optional)	Tuesday Sessions 3 and 4
☐ **Physical Education** (optional)	Wednesday Session 4, Friday Session 4
☐ **Food Technology** (optional)	Friday Sessions 1 and 2
☐ **Textiles and Fashion** (optional)	Wednesday Session 4, Friday Session 4
☐ **Latin** (optional)	Thursday Session 2, Friday Session 3
☐ **Art** (optional)	Tuesday Sessions 3 and 4
☐ **Computer Studies** (optional)	Friday Sessions 1 and 2
☐ **Geography** (optional)	Wednesday Session 4, Friday Session 4
☐ **Business Studies** (optional)	Monday Session 2, Wednesday Session 2
☐ **Music** (optional)	Thursday Session 2, Friday Session 3

	Monday	Tuesday	Wednesday	Thursday	Friday
Session 1					
Morning break					
Session 2					
Lunch					
Session 3					
Afternoon break					
Session 4					

Fruit and Vegetables

Harvest Festival is a Christian festival.
It is on a Sunday in September or October. It is to celebrate the harvest.
People take flowers and food to school or to church.

This is a traditional decoration for Harvest Festival. What is it called?
Colour the fruit and vegetables in the baskets and find out.

It's a ....

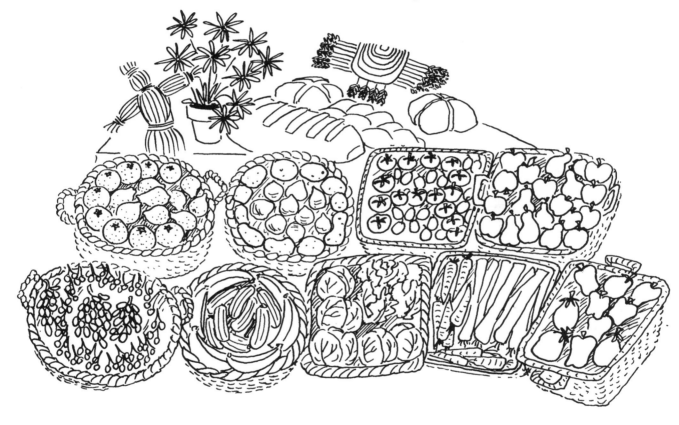

Colour the fruit and vegetables these colours.

oranges	orange	**apples**	red	**cabbages**	dark green
lemons	yellow	**pears**	green	**lettuces**	light green
potatoes	brown	**grapes**	green	**carrots**	orange
beetroot	purple	**cherries**	red	**leeks**	green
tomatoes	red	**bananas**	yellow	**peppers**	red
plums	purple	**courgettes**	green	**aubergines**	purple

Harvest Boxes

After the Harvest Festival, children take boxes of food to elderly people.

Can you find the right box of food for each person? Write the name of each person on the correct box.

A *I'd like some apples but I don't want any ketchup.* **Mrs Brown**

B *I'd like some jam and potatoes but I don't want any cauliflowers.* **Mr Clare**

C *I'd like some cheese but I don't want any potatoes or onions.* **Mrs Gower**

D *I'd like some onions but I don't want any grapes or biscuits.* **Mr Short**

E *I'd like a cake and some tomatoes but I don't want any bread.* **Mrs Watts**

F *I'd like some oranges but I don't want any eggs.* **Mr Flint**

There is one box left over. Who is it for?
Take the first letter of each thing in the box and make the name of the person.

Rosh Hashanah Traditions

**Rosh Hashanah is the Jewish New Year. It is the most important time in the Jewish year.
Rosh Hashanah is in September or October.**

What do you know about Rosh Hashanah?
Look at the pictures and read the sentences. Choose the correct verb in each sentence.

Example:  The Jewish new year (*begins*) / *ends*
in the Autumn.

Before Rosh Hashanah people
r *cook* / **s** *clean* their houses.

People **h** *give* / **i** *take* cards to
their friends.

They **o** *go* / **p** *bring* to
the synagogue.

They **e** *talk* / **f** *ask* God to forgive
all the bad things they do.

They **a** *eat* / **b** *write* honey and
apples. This is for a sweet and
happy new year.

Leshanah
Tovah
Tikatev!

They **q** *fly* / **r** *say* 'Leshanah Tovah
Tikatev' (Happy New Year).

You can hear this musical
instrument in the synagogue
at Rosh Hashanah. What is it?
Write the letter of each correct
verb in the grid.

1	2	3	4	5	6

Bad Things

Rosh Hashanah is the Jewish new year.
People ask God to forgive them for all the bad things they have done.

Some people are talking about the bad things they did last year.
Put the verbs in the past tense and write them in the grid.

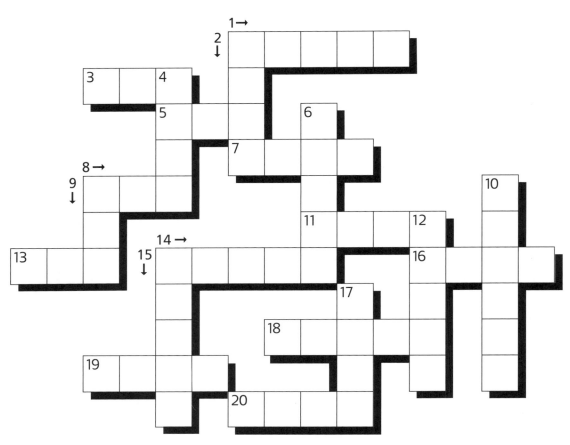

I **1** .... (drink) some beer at my friend's party.

I **2** .... (draw) a funny picture of my teacher.

I **5** .... (eat) my brother's sweets and

4 .... (say) it **3** .... (be) my sister.

I **6** .... (break) my dad's computer and I didn't tell him.

I **7** .... (wear) my brother's jumper without asking his permission.

I **8** .... (hide) my sister's favourite T-shirt when she was going to a party.

I **9** .... (hit) my little brother when he annoyed me.

I **10** .... (forget) my best friend's birthday.

I **11** .... (keep) some money that was supposed to be for charity.

I **12** .... (throw) my friend's homework in the bin.

I **13** .... (put) a spider in my sister's hair.

I **14** .... (swear) at my dad.

I **15** .... (spend) my school lunch money on crisps and sweets.

I **16** .... (hurt) my friend's feelings by saying she was fat.

I **17** .... (sell) my brother's Walkman to my friend because I needed some money.

I **18** .... (steal) five pounds from my mum's purse.

I **19** .... (go) to my friend's house instead of doing my homework.

I **20** .... (tell) my mum a lie.

What Time Is It?

The last Saturday in October is the last day of British Summer Time.
At midnight, British people put their clocks back one hour.

These are the times on Saturday. What time is it at the same time of day on Sunday?
Write the times and draw them on the clocks and watches.

Saturday	Sunday

Example: (ten o'clock) *nine o'clock*
....

1. (twelve o'clock)
....

2. (half past six)
....

3. (quarter to four)
....

4. (quarter past seven)
....

5. (ten to eight)
....

6. (ten past eleven)
....

7. (twenty-five past one)
....

8. (twenty to three)
....

9. (five past nine)
....

10. (twenty to two)
....

11. (five to five)
....

12. (twenty-five to ten)
....

An Hour Ahead

Today is the last Saturday in October. Tonight the clocks go back one hour, but David and his family have forgotten.

This is David's plan for tomorrow.

Sunday

8 a.m.	take the dog for a walk
9 a.m.	have breakfast
10 a.m.	go to my friend's house
11 a.m.	play football
12 a.m.	wash Mum's car
1 p.m.	have lunch
2 p.m.	tidy my bedroom
3 p.m.	do my homework
4 p.m.	ride my bike
5 p.m.	play computer games
6 p.m.	have dinner
7 p.m.	read a magazine
8 p.m.	watch TV
10 p.m.	go to bed

Read the sentences about what David will do tomorrow. Which sentences are true and which are false? If the sentence is false, write a true sentence. (Don't forget that David is one hour ahead of his plan.)

For example:

At eight o'clock David will take the dog for a walk.
False. At eight o'clock David will have breakfast.
....

1. At six o'clock David will read a magazine.

....
....

2. At five o'clock David will ride his bike.

....
....

3. At twelve o'clock David will wash his Mum's car.

....
....

4. At two o'clock David will do his homework.

....
....

5. At ten o'clock in the morning David will go to his friend's house.

....
....

6. At four o'clock David will do his homework.

....
....

7. At seven o'clock David will read a magazine.

....
....

8. At three o'clock David will tidy his room.

....
....

9. At seven o'clock in the evening David will watch TV.

....
....

10. At eleven o'clock David will play football.

....
....

Hallowe'en Costumes

Hallowe'en is the 31st of October. It is the night of ghosts and evil spirits.
In Britain, lots of people go to Hallowe'en parties. They wear spooky costumes.

Look at these costumes.
Label the clothes with these words.

coat   cloak   dress
gloves   hat   jumper
leggings   mask
shirt   shoes   slippers
trousers

witch

1. ....
2. ....
3. ....
4. ....

vampire

5. ....
6. ....
7. ....

cat

8. ....
9. ....
10. ....
11. ....
12. ....

Now find the words in the wordsearch.
The letters left over in lines 1, 2, 3 and 4
spell four more Hallowe'en characters.
Write the words under the pictures.

1	g	d	h	j	o	l	s	t
	t	r	o	u	s	e	r	s
	d	e	f	m	c	g	a	l
2	b	s	a	p	o	g	t	i
	l	s	x	e	a	i	y	p
	s	h	i	r	t	n	q	p
3	a	l	i	e	n	g	m	e
	g	l	o	v	e	s	a	r
	s	h	o	e	s	h	s	s
	u	z	c	l	o	a	k	w
4	m	o	n	s	t	t	e	r

1. ....
2. ....
3. ....
4. ....

Hallowe'en Apples

Apple peel

There are lots of superstitions at Hallowe'en. Here is one. Try it at home!

Solve the anagrams and write a girl's name and a boy's name for each letter.

girl's name **boy's name**

Peel an apple.

Throw the peel over your shoulder.

The peel makes the first letter of your future boyfriend's or girlfriend's name.

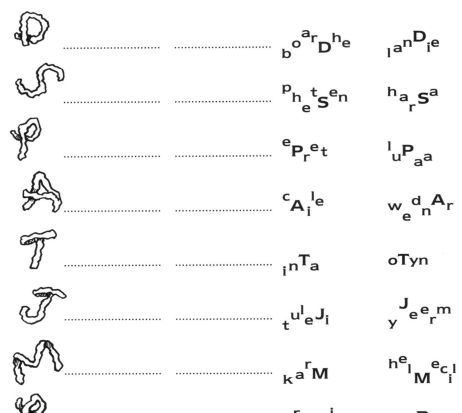

.... $b o^a{}_r D^h e$ $_l a n D_i e$

.... $^p_h{}^t_e S^e n$ $h_a{}_r S^a$

.... $^e P_r{}^e t$ $^l u P_a{}^a$

.... $^c A_i{}^l e$ $w^d_e{}_n A_r$

.... $_i n T_a$ $o T y n$

.... $_t u^l_e J_i$ $y^J_e{}^e_r{}^m$

.... $_k a^r M$ $h^e_l M^e_c{}_i{}^l$

.... $d^r_a{}_c h^i R$ $c_h{}^e R_a{}_l$

.... $^a_l C_o n_i{}^r e$ $^t h_r o C_p{}_r{}^i e_s h$

Apple bobbing

Apple bobbing is a game you can play at a Hallowe'en party.

Look at the pictures and read the instructions. Try it at home!

1 Fill a bowl with water.

2 Put lots of newspaper on the table.

3 Put some apples in the water.

4 Try to catch an apple in your mouth. This is difficult.

Are You Superstitious?

What does Hallowe'en mean for you? Choose your favourite description for each picture.

1

▲ Isabelle is reading a recipe for pumpkin cake. ☐

☻ Isabelle is reading a magic spell. ☐

2

▲ The black cat is crossing in front of Phillip. ☐

☻ The black cat is bringing Phillip good luck. ☐

3

☻ The pumpkin lanterns are frightening away evil spirits. ☐

▲ The pumpkin lanterns look nice at the Hallowe'en party. ☐

4

☻ Debbie's future husband is going to appear in the mirror. ☐

▲ Debbie is brushing her hair. She is going to bed soon. ☐

5

☻ Ryan is looking at a ghost. ☐

▲ Ryan is watching a horror film. ☐

6

▲ Stephen is playing a Hallowe'en party game. ☐

☻ Stephen is going to meet a girl whose name begins with Z. ☐

7

▲ Laura has got 20p in her cake. She is going to buy some sweets. ☐

☻ Laura has got a lucky coin in her cake. She is going to be rich. ☐

8

▲ Scott is looking for his lost contact lens. ☐

☻ Scott is reading his fortune in the tea leaves. ☐

9

☻ Stacey is going to have seven years bad luck. ☐

▲ Stacey needs to buy a new mirror. ☐

10

☻ Andy is all alone in a haunted house. ☐

▲ Andy is using a candle because there is a power cut. ☐

Now ask your teacher for the analysis.

Who's the Thief?

This was a really good Hallowe'en party. However, at midnight someone stole all the money from people's coats in the hall.
Two minutes before the theft, the security camera broke.
This is the last picture on the camera.

PC Williams found these teeth in the hall near the coats.

These are the suspects.

What were you doing at midnight on the 31st of October?

I was dancing with the gorilla.

Hannah

I was watching the karaoke. I was standing next to the bat.

Kerry

I was eating some cake. I was standing next to the table.

Darren

I was singing karaoke with the skeleton.

Vicky

I was queueing for the toilet. I was next to the frog.

Steve

I was bobbing for apples with the astronaut.

Naima

I was talking to the mummy.

Chris

PC Williams is writing a police report. Can you complete the report for her? You will need some of these words.

alien	astronaut	bat	cat
Frankenstein		frog	ghost
gorilla	mummy		pumpkin
skeleton	Dracula		witch

It can't have been *Hannah* because *she must be the witch.*

It can't have been .... because
....

It can't have been .... because
....

It can't have been .... because
....

It can't have been .... because
....

It can't have been .... because
....

It must have been .... because
....

Guys

Bonfire Night is the 5th of November. British people celebrate with bonfires and fireworks. Children make guys to burn on the bonfire. A guy is a model of Guy Fawkes. Another name for Bonfire Night is Guy Fawkes' Night.

Sam, Paul, Gloria and Marcus are making guys for Bonfire Night.

D. This is ....'s guy.

A. This is ....'s guy.

B. This is ....'s guy.

C. This is ....'s guy.

Find Sam's guy. He's tall and thin.

Find Paul's guy. He's small and fat.

Find Gloria's guy. He's got a long nose and a big black hat.

Find Marcus's guy. He's got a long moustache and a long beard.

Which guy do you like?
I like .... 's guy.

Sam

Paul

Gloria

Marcus

Where are the Pets?

Lots of pets live in this house.

Morgan   Joey   Tiger   Captain   Snowy   Bubbles

Sandy   Jaguar   Ben   Toby   Waffles   Sam

The animals don't like Bonfire Night. They are frightened of the fireworks.
They are hiding in the house.

1. Which animal is behind the sofa?

   It's ....

2. Which animal is under the bed?

   It's ....

3. Which animal is on the chair?

   It's ....

4. Which animal is on the cupboard?

   It's ....

5. Which animal is in the drawer?

   It's ....

6. Which animal is behind the wardrobe?

   It's ....

7. Which animal is between the cooker and the cupboard?

   It's ....

8. Which animal is on the shelf?

   It's ....

9. Which animal is under the table?

   It's ....

10. Which animal is behind the bed?

    It's ....

11. Which animal is in the bath?

    It's ....

12. Which animal is on the fridge?

    It's ....

Bonfire Night Safety

On Bonfire Night, lots of people have bonfires and fireworks in their gardens.

Fireworks and bonfires are dangerous. These are the rules for Bonfire Night safety.
But the sentences are in the wrong order. Put them in the right order.

For example:

near stand Don't fireworks the

Don't stand near the fireworks.
....

Look at the sentences with **Don't**.
Draw a cross on the picture.

fireworks Don't throw

....

box fireworks metal Keep in your a

....

Don't near bonfire the fireworks put

....

in house light the fireworks Don't

....

light with a fireworks Don't match

....

taper Light fireworks a with

....

house in Keep pets the your

....

cook Don't food bonfire on the

....

warm clothes Wear

....

The Story of Guy Fawkes

Bonfire Night is also called Guy Fawkes' Night.

Read the questions about Guy Fawkes. Find the correct answer to each question.

1 Is this a story from the nineteenth century?

2 Were Guy Fawkes and his friends Protestants?

3 Were there religious problems between the Catholics and the Protestants?

4 Was there a law saying that Catholics weren't allowed to go to church?

5 Did Guy Fawkes and his friends decide to kill King James?

6 Did Guy Fawkes put explosives in the Houses of Parliament?

7 Was the date the 11th of December 1605?

8 Did the plan succeed?

9 Did the king forgive Guy Fawkes and his friends?

10 Do British people celebrate Guy Fawkes' Night with bonfires and fireworks?

11 Do children make models of King James and burn them on the bonfires?

12 Are the models called 'guys'?

13 Are ice-cream and salad popular on Bonfire Night?

E Yes, they do.

T Yes, he did.

B Yes, there were.

B Yes, they are.

E Yes, there was.

R Yes, they did.

R No, it isn't. It's a story from the seventeenth century.

A No, it didn't. The king's soldiers discovered the plan.

O No, they weren't. They were Catholics.

T No, he didn't. He decided to kill Guy Fawkes and his friends.

Y No, they aren't. Toffee apples, soup and baked potatoes are popular.

C No, it wasn't. It was the 5th of November 1605.

S No, they don't. They make models of Guy Fawkes.

Guy Fawkes wasn't the leader of the Gunpowder Plot. Write the letter of each answer under the correct number. You can find the name of the leader of the Gunpowder Plot.

1	2	3	4	5	6

7	8	9	10	11	12	13

Toffee Apples

Toffee apples are popular on Bonfire Night.

Yasmin and Tom are making toffee apples. Read what they say and write the amounts next to the ingredients.

We need more sugar than butter.

We need less vinegar than water.

We need the same number of wooden skewers as apples.

You will need:	
.... soft brown sugar	**10**
.... butter	**10**
.... vinegar	**350 grams**
.... water	**450 grams**
.... apples	**5 millilitres**
.... wooden skewers	**150 millilitres**

This is the recipe. Write the adverbs in the sentences.

carefully

immediately

lightly

neatly

occasionally

rapidly

slowly

1

_ _ _ _ _ _ _ oil a large baking tray.

2

Put all the ingredients a large saucepan. Place over a low heat and bring _ _ _ _ _ _ to the boil. Stir _ _ _ _ _ _ _ _ _ _ _ with a wooden spoon.

3

When the sugar has dissolved, boil the toffee _ _ _ _ _ _ _ for 10 minutes over a high heat.

4

Drop a teaspoon of toffee in a saucer of cold water. If the toffee sets _ _ _ _ _ _ _ _ _ _ _ , it is ready.

5

Push a wooden skewer into each apple. _ _ _ _ _ _ _ _ dip the apples in the toffee.

6

Place the toffee apples on the baking tray. Leave them to set.

7

Cut squares of cellophane. Wrap the apples _ _ _ _ _ in the cellophane.

Preparing for Diwali

**Diwali is the Hindu festival of light. In India, the festival lasts for five days.
In Britain, Hindus celebrate for a weekend. Diwali is in October or November.**

Sheetal and her family are preparing for Diwali.

Read what Sheetal says. Who is in each picture?

My auntie is cooking *dhokla*.
My big brother is writing a Diwali card.
My little cousin is taking food to the table.
My older cousin is lighting a *diva*.
My mum and dad are dancing the *dandia raas*.
My little sister is wrapping a present.
My big sister is making a *rangoli* pattern.
My uncle is buying fireworks for the Diwali party.
My little brother is helping with the cooking.

1 Anita Sanjay

Sheetal's auntie

....

2 Anand

....

3 Rahim

....

4 Tara

....

5 Deepa

....

6 Nilesh

....

7 Geeta

....

8 Ranjit Priya

....

Now write everyone's names on Sheetal's family tree.

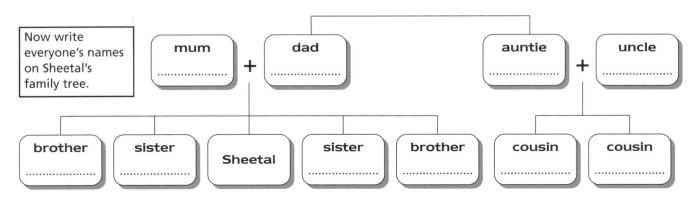

| mum | **+** | dad | | auntie | **+** | uncle |
| .... | | .... | | .... | | .... |

| brother | sister | Sheetal | sister | brother | cousin | cousin |
| .... | .... | | .... | .... | .... | .... |

Rama and Sita

Diwali celebrates the time when Rama came home to become king.
Rama is the Hindu god Vishnu in human form.

Read the story of Rama and Sita.

In the city of Ayodhya, Prince Rama lived with his wife Sita and with Sita's brother Lakshman. The king's wife didn't like Rama, so the king sent Rama, Sita and Lakshman away for 14 years. They lived in the forest and were happy.

Ravana was the wicked king of Lanka. He wanted Sita to be his wife, so he kidnapped her. He took her to the island of Lanka in his flying chariot. A bird tried to help Sita, but Ravana shot it.

Rama and Lakshman went to look for Sita. The injured bird told them that she was on the island of Lanka. Rama and Lakshman met Hanuman, the monkey king. Hanuman and the monkeys travelled with Rama and Lakshman. When they came to the sea, the monkeys built a bridge over the sea to Lanka. There was a big battle. Rama killed Ravana and rescued Sita.

Now the 14 years were over. Rama, Sita and Lakshman returned to Ayodhya. The people welcomed them with small lamps called divas. Rama and Sita became king and queen.

Read the clues and fill in the gaps with these words: *who, that, where*.
Do the crossword.

1. The person ......*who*........ went to the forest with Rama and Sita

2. The king .... helped Rama and Lakshman cross the sea

3. The animals .... built the bridge

4. The island .... Ravana lived

5. The place .... Rama, Sita and Lakshman lived after they left Ayodhya

6. The person .... kidnapped Sita

7. The animal .... tried to help Sita

8. The lamps .... the people lit to welcome Sita and Raman home

9. The person .... killed Ravana

10. The city .... Rama and Sita lived

11. The person ....was married to Rama

Winter Weather

Look at the letters in the pictures and make eight winter weather words.
The words are all in the <u>wrong pictures</u>.
Write each word under the correct picture.

1

It's ....

2

It's ....

3

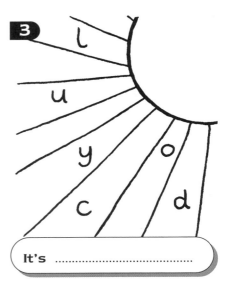

It's ....

4

It's ....

5

It's ....

6

It's ....

7

It's ....

8

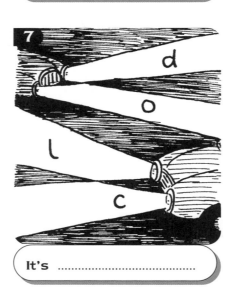

It's ....

Who Likes Winter?

Some of these six people like winter and some don't.
Choose the answer to each question to find out who likes winter and who doesn't.

> No, he doesn't.   No, he isn't.   No, she doesn't.
> No, he won't.   No, he wouldn't.
> Yes, she can.   Yes, she is.   Yes, she will.   Yes, he has.
> Yes, he can.   Yes, she would.   Yes, she has.

1. It's very foggy this morning and the school bus might be late. Does Eleanor go to school?

No, she doesn't.

2. Is Eleanor going to stay at home all day?

....

3. Ian is reading about the North Pole. Would he like to go to the North Pole?

....

4. Ian is playing football tomorrow, but it is going to snow tonight. Will he still play?

....

5. Mike's class is going skiing. Can Mike ski?

....

6. Has Mike got some skis?

....

7. Catherine's mum wants her to take the dog for a walk. It's windy and rainy. Will Catherine take the dog for a walk?

....

8. Has Catherine got an umbrella and a raincoat?

....

9. The pond froze last night. Can Angela skate?

....

10. Would Angela like a pair of skates for Christmas?

....

11. It's been snowing and Paul is going to school. Is he good at walking in the snow?

....

12. Does Paul like playing in the snow?

....

Answer the questions:

Does Eleanor like the winter?

....

Does Ian like the winter?

....

Does Mike like the winter?

....

Does Catherine like the winter?

....

Does Angela like the winter?

....

Does Paul like the winter?

....

Advent Calendar

Advent calendars are popular in December. You can count the days from the 1st of December to the 25th of December – Christmas Day. Every day you open a door and find a picture.

Look at the advent calendar. Write the names of the pictures next to the numbers.

1. holly
2. cracker
3. Father Christmas
4. hat
5. Christmas cake
6. bell
7. donkey
8. snowflake
9. bauble
10. kings
11. candle
12. robin
13. turkey
14. snowman
15. sleigh
16. shepherd
17. reindeer
18. star
19. Christmas tree
20. stocking
21. Christmas card
22. present
23. Christmas pudding
24. angel
25. baby Jesus

twenty-one	*Christmas card*	six	....	eighteen	....
sixteen	....	fourteen	....	twelve	....
seven	....	one	....	nine	....
eleven	....	twenty-five	....	twenty-three	....
twenty-four	....	seventeen	....	two	....
three	....	ten	....	fifteen	....
thirteen	....	twenty-two	....	twenty	....
eight	....	five	....		
nineteen	....	four	....		

Christmas Show

Jonathan's school is doing a Christmas show. Lots of people are helping.
Find the words in the wordsearch and complete the sentences.

1

Martine is ..... *acting* .....
in the Nativity ..... *play* .....

2

Alistair is .p.....
the .t.....

3

Rebecca is .p.....
the .c.....

4

Ranjeet is .p.....
the .s.....

5

Anna is .p.....
the .d.....

6

One cold
Christmas night
In the
silvery moonlight.

Liam is .r.....
a .p.....

7

Adelle is .s.....
a .c.....

8

Paul is .h..... with
the .l.....

9

Danielle is .g.....
presents to the .c.....

10

Richard is .s.....
the .t.....

11

Emma is .m.....
the .c.....

12

Oliver is m.....
the .m.....

C	O	S	T	U	M	E	S	F	A	S	T	M
P	L	A	Y	I	N	G	P	H	E	C	R	A
A	D	C	C	C	H	I	L	D	R	E	N	S
I	R	A	P	U	E	H	A	T	P	N	S	K
N	U	R	L	R	L	R	Y	R	U	E	E	S
T	M	O	A	T	P	L	I	U	L	R	L	I
I	S	L	Y	A	I	I	N	M	L	Y	L	N
N	M	A	K	I	N	G	G	P	I	I	I	G
G	I	V	I	N	G	H	S	E	N	T	N	I
P	O	E	M	S	M	T	A	T	G	S	G	N
T	I	C	K	E	T	S	A	C	T	I	N	G
M	A	K	I	N	G	R	E	A	D	I	N	G

**What is Jonathan in the Christmas show? Look
at the letters left over in the wordsearch and
write the words under the correct picture.**

A
.....

B
.....

C
.....

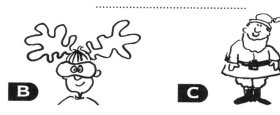

Giant Christmas Crossword

Across →

1.
   and a
   HAPPY NEW YEAR
   (5, 9)

8.  (3)

9. "Shall we dress up as reindeer for the Christmas party?"
   "....., let's dress up as elves." (2)

10.  (5)

11.
    I'm ugly but you are .... than me.
    (6)

12.  (6)

14. "Let's ..... up at 4 o'clock on Christmas morning to open our presents." (3)

16.  (3)

18. *This game is for 2-4 players. You need a dice and counters. The first player to throw a six starts. You must not land on the same square as your opponent* (5)

21.
    La, la....
    (2)

22. Anagram of **AWNE** (boy's name). (4)

23.
    ..... Claus (5)

25.
    I'm ....
    (5)

26.  (5)

27. "Why don't ..... go carol singing?"
    "That's a good idea." (2)

28.  (5)

32.  (3)

33.  (9)

37. "How about playing some ..... after Christmas dinner?" (5)

39.  (8)

41.  Do you want to .... the Christmas cake? (4)

43. The 25th of December is Christmas ..... (3)

44. Ducks quack, horses neigh and dogs ..... (4)

45. "Shall we ..... the film on television now?" (5)

48. David is very happy. ..... loves his Christmas presents. (2)

49.  The three wise ..... (3)

50. Christmas ..... a very happy time of year. (2)

51. The day before Christmas Day is Christmas ..... (3)

52.  The snowman is ..... the table. (2)

53.  (5)

55.  (5)

57.  (8, 5)

Down ↓

1.  (5, 4)

2.  (7)

3. A kind of music. (3)

4.  Carol ..... (7)

5. "What shall we do now?" "How about ..... the Christmas cake?" (6)

6.  This is ..... angel. (2)

7.  (4)

10.  (4)

13. The colour of 7 down. (6)

15.  (6)

17. Japanese money. (3)

19. "I want to ..... lots of money to buy Christmas presents." "Why don't you do some babysitting?" (4)

20.  (5)

22. 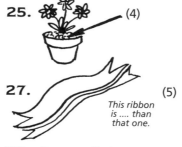 (3)

24. In my family, we ..... love Christmas. (3)

25.  (4)

27. (5) This ribbon is .... than that one.

29. "I ..... really looking forward to Christmas." (2)

30. My teacher's name is ..... Lloyd. (4)

31. 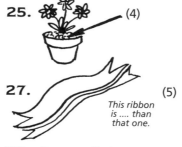 (4)

34. **10** (3)

35.  At Christmas, people ..... a lot. (3)

36. "Would you like a mince pie ..... a slice of Christmas cake?" (2)

38.  (4)

39.  Christmas ..... (7)

40.  (6)

42. "....., dear. I don't like any of my Christmas presents." (2)

44.  (4)

45. "Let's go to church on Christmas morning. ..... all like singing carols." (2)

46. I always get ..... apple and a tangerine in my Christmas stocking. (2)

47.  (6)

49. My mum and dad are giving ..... a new bike for Christmas. (2)

52. "On Christmas Eve, shall we watch television ..... play games?" (2)

53. Sandra is going to stay with ..... Grandma for Christmas. (3)

54.  (3)

55.  (3)

56.  The turkey is ..... the oven. (2)

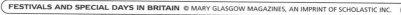

A Christmas Carol

a story by Charles Dickens (1812–1870)

Read the story.

Ebenezer Scrooge is a money lender. He is very rich but he is also very mean. He has no friends. He pays his employee, Bob Cratchit, a very low wage. He doesn't believe in celebrating Christmas. His nephew, Fred, invites him for Christmas dinner but he refuses.

One Christmas Eve, Scrooge is visited by three ghosts. The ghosts show him his life in the past, the present and the future.

These are the three ghosts and the things that they show to Scrooge.
Write the number of each sentence in the picture of the correct ghost.

The Ghost of Christmas Past	The Ghost of Christmas Present	The Ghost of Christmas Future

1. All the shops in London are busy and there are decorations everywhere. Some people are buying food for Christmas dinner and some people are going to church.

2. When Scrooge was a boy, he went to boarding school. All the boys went home for Christmas but Scrooge had to stay at school on his own.

3. One Christmas, Scrooge will die all alone.

4. Some poor people will steal his clothes and sell them.

5. Bob Cratchit is coming home from church with Tiny Tim. Tiny Tim is his youngest child and he is very ill.

6. The Cratchit family are very poor. They are having a very small Christmas dinner but they are happy because they love each other.

7. Nobody will visit Scrooge's grave because nobody loves him.

8. Scrooge started work. His boss was very kind and gave a big Christmas party. Scrooge had a great time.

9. Tiny Tim will die because the family is too poor to pay for a doctor. Bob Cratchit will be very unhappy.

10. Scrooge fell in love with a girl, but he loved money more than he loved her so she left him.

11. Scrooge's nephew Fred is having a Christmas party. Fred's family and friends are playing music, singing and playing games.

12. The girl married another man and had lots of children.

What happens next?

What do you think will happen next in the story?

a Scrooge will die and become an evil ghost.

b Scrooge will become kinder and pay Bob Cratchit more money.

c Scrooge will give all his money to Bob Cratchit and Fred.

New Year in Scotland

The biggest New Year's celebrations in Britain are in Scotland.
Scottish people have a special word for New Year. Do the puzzle to find out what it is.

Match up the two parts of each word. Write the words under the pictures.

BAG   WHI   CHAM   FIRE   EDIN   DAN   CO   PA

PAGNE   RTY   CE   SKY   PIPES   WORKS   BURGH   AL

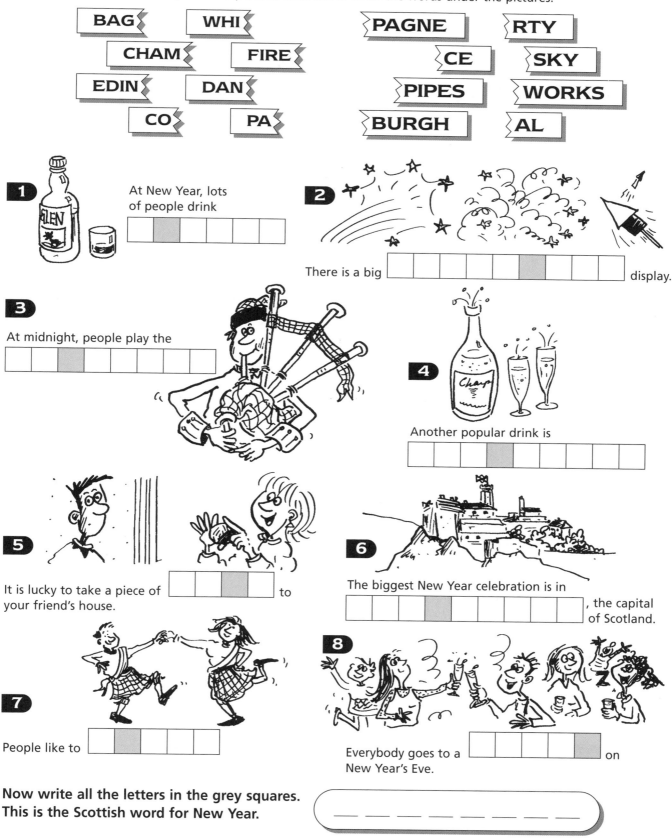

1 At New Year, lots of people drink ☐☐▨☐☐☐

2 There is a big ☐☐☐☐☐☐▨☐☐☐ display.

3 At midnight, people play the ☐☐▨☐☐☐☐☐☐

4 Another popular drink is ☐☐☐☐☐▨☐☐☐☐☐

5 It is lucky to take a piece of ☐☐▨☐ to your friend's house.

6 The biggest New Year celebration is in ☐☐☐☐▨☐☐☐☐, the capital of Scotland.

7 People like to ☐☐▨☐☐☐

8 Everybody goes to a ☐☐☐☐▨ on New Year's Eve.

**Now write all the letters in the grey squares.
This is the Scottish word for New Year.**

_ _ _ _ _ _ _ _ _

New Year's Resolutions

Lots of people make New Year's resolutions. They try to do positive things in the New Year.

These people are all making New Year's resolutions. Match the pictures to the resolutions.

a
I'm going to play football
every week.

b
I'm going to go scuba diving.

c
I'm going to learn to play the violin.

d
I'm going to buy a new stereo.

e
I'm going to do my homework every day.

f
I'm going to save my money.

g
I'm going to make new friends.

h
I'm going to go to Spain.

i
I'm going to tidy my room
every week.

j
I'm going to eat healthy food.

What are your New Year's resolutions? Write three things.	I'm going to ....
	I'm going to ....
	I'm going to ....

Celebrating the New Year

**The New Year has been celebrated for thousands of years.
Every culture has its own New Year festival. Here are some New Year festivals from the past and also some New Year festivals that are celebrated in Britain by people from different cultures.**

Choose the correct word in each sentence. Find the words in the wordsearch.
The letters left over spell a message for you.

Ancient festivals

Ancient Egyptian New Year
The Ancient Egyptian New Year was (1) **celebrated/happened** in September. There was a big procession along the River Nile. The procession was (2) **led/gone** by the Pharaoh. Trumpets, drums and tambourines were (3) **listened/played**.

Roman New Year
During Roman times a new calendar was (4) **arrived/invented** and the New Year was (5) **run/moved** from March to January. At New Year gifts were (6) **sent/made** to friends and even to the Emperor. Funny costumes were (7) **danced/worn** at parties.

Celtic New Year
The Celtic New Year was in October and was called *Samhain*, which means 'summer's end'. Bonfires were (8) **shone/burned** and people danced around them.

Modern festivals

Jewish New Year
The Jewish New Year is called *Rosh Hashanah* and it is (9) **taken/celebrated** in October. Special services are (10) **held/got** at the synagogue. Honey and fish are (11) **eaten/looked** – honey is for a sweet year and fish is for a year of plenty. Special round loaves of bread are (12) **boiled/baked**. People's houses are (13) **done/cleaned** and new clothes are (14) **bought/given** for children.

Hogmany
Hogmanay is the Scottish word for New Year's Eve. People go to parties. At midnight an old song called 'Auld Lang Syne' is (15) **sung/seen**. There is also a tradition called 'first footing'. If you are (16) **shouted/visited** by a man with dark hair you will have good luck in the next year.

Muslim New Year
The Muslim New Year is called the *Day of the Hijrah*. It remembers the journey (17) **made/gone** by Muhammad from Mecca to Jerusalem. Children are (18) **played/given** presents and new clothes.

Hindu New Year

Many Hindus celebrate New Year in October, at the same time as *Diwali*, the festival of light. Little lamps called *divas* are (19) **lost/lit** and they are (20) **swum/floated** on lakes and ponds. The story of Rama and Sita is (21) **talked/told** to children.

Chinese New Year
There is a big Chinese New Year festival in London every January or February. Dragon and lion dances are (22) **performed/laughed**. Evil spirits are (23) **frightened/haunted** away with firecrackers. Red clothes are (24) **put/worn** for good luck.

S	H	A	H	L	I	T	F	E	L	E	D
E	F	C	E	L	E	B	R	A	T	E	D
N	L	E	L	V	I	S	I	T	E	D	P
T	O	L	D	P	P	Y	G	E	N	I	E
P	A	E	W	O	R	N	H	N	B	N	R
L	T	B	O	U	G	H	T	E	A	V	F
A	E	R	R	G	I	V	E	N	K	E	O
Y	D	A	N	W	S	U	N	G	E	N	R
E	Y	T	B	U	R	N	E	D	D	T	M
D	E	E	M	O	V	E	D	A	R	E	E
M	A	D	E	C	L	E	A	N	E	D	D

The Muslim Year

Ramadan and Id-ul-Fitr are important times in the Muslim year. Ramadan is the month when Muslims fast (they don't eat or drink in the daytime). Id-ul-Fitr is the big festival at the end of Ramadan.

The Muslim calendar is different from the western calendar. There are twelve months, but each month begins with the new moon.

These are the months of the Muslim year, but they are in the wrong order. Colour the letters to find the order of the months.

For example:
Ramadan is number 9, so it is the ninth month

Colour the letters these colours:
1 = yellow	**5** = orange	**9** = grey
2 = red	**6** = purple	**10** = light green
3 = light blue	**7** = brown	**11** = dark green
4 = dark blue	**8** = pink	**12** = black

Month	Number
Ramadan	*ninth month*
Dhul-Qa'dah	
Jumada-l-Ula	
Rajab	
Dhul-Hijjah	
Muharram	
Rabi ath-Thani	
Jumada-th-Thaniyyah	
Shawwal	
Rabi al-Awwal	
Safar	
Sha'ban	

Fast and Festival

Ramadan and Id-ul-Fitr are very important times in the Muslim year.
Ramadan is one of the months in the Muslim calendar. Each new month begins with
the new moon. Id-ul-Fitr is the festival at the end of Ramadan.

Nadia is talking about Ramadan and Id-ul-Fitr.
Read what she says and fill in the missing
time words. Write the words in the text and
in the grid. (The grid will help you to choose
the correct words.)

at (x 3)	before (x 3)
during (x 4)	first (x 1)	later (x 1)

at (x 3) before (x 3)
during (x 4) first (x 1) later (x 1)
often (x 1) on (x 2) until (x 3)
when (x 2) while (x 4)

12 .... the month of Ramadan we can't eat or drink

16 .... the day. This is called fasting. We have to wait

22 .... the evening to eat. **4** .... sunset,

18 .... we have a snack and **7** .... we have

a main meal. All eating must finish **2** .... the sun rises.

20 .... we are fasting we learn to be patient.

It is very difficult not to eat or drink **3** .... the day. Not all Muslims

have to fast **13** .... Ramadan. Very old people don't fast and children

don't have to fast **6** .... they are twelve years old. People who are on

a journey can eat **5** .... they are travelling. Women don't fast

19 .... they are expecting a baby. Ill people don't fast but they must

fast **1** .... they are healthy again. **23** .... we are fasting,

we pray more than usual and read the Qur'an more.

Id-ul-Fitr is the festival **8** .... the end of Ramadan. It begins

10 .... the first day of the next month. **17** .... Id-ul-Fitr, we

give money for the poor, so that everyone will be able to celebrate the festival.

9 .... the night **15** .... Id, we **24** .... don't go to

bed. We stay up all night and wait **14** .... the new moon appears.

21 .... we can see the new moon the festival begins.

11 .... Id we visit our friends and have parties. We
give presents and cards and we eat special cakes and sweets.

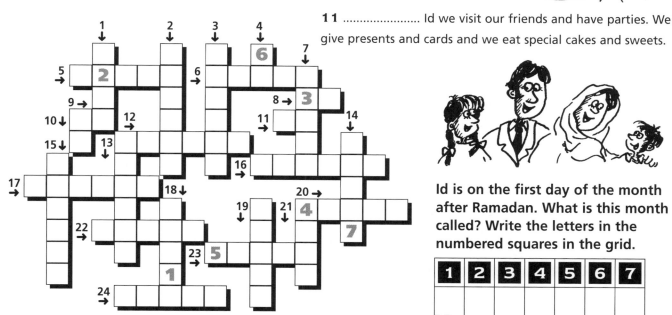

**Id is on the first day of the month
after Ramadan. What is this month
called? Write the letters in the
numbered squares in the grid.**

1	2	3	4	5	6	7

Animal Years

The Chinese New Year is in January or February.
In the Chinese calendar, every year has the name of an animal: rat, snake, tiger, etc.
There are 12 animals. If you are born in the year of the tiger, you have the tiger's personality.

These are the Chinese years. Find the animals and write the adjectives in the table.

Year	Animal	Personality
2 February 1984–19 February 1985	rat	*happy, sociable*
20 February 1985–8 February 1986	ox	
9 February 1986–28 January 1987	tiger	
29 January 1987–16 February 1988	rabbit	
17 February 1988–5 February 1989	dragon	
6 February 1989–26 January 1990	snake	
27 January 1990–14 February 1991	horse	
15 February 1991–3 February 1992	ram	
4 February 1992–22 January 1993	monkey	
23 January 1993–9 February 1994	rooster	
10 February 1994–30 January 1995	dog	
31 January 1995–18 February 1996	pig	

When is your birthday? Which animal are you?
Do the words for your animal describe your personality?
Write four words to describe yourself.

Code Breaker

It is an old Chinese superstition that whatever happens on New Year's Day will happen for the whole year.

Can you solve the codes for these words? Each number is always the same letter.
Then when you have all the words, write each word in the correct sentence.

bad   cold   cut   death   good   happy   knife   money   rains   red   snows   year

20	7	13

18	19	16

9	2	13

12	5	5	13

8	2	7	9

18	5	17	13

13	2	7	16	4

4	7	6	6	8

14	11	10	15	2

3	5	11	2	8

9	7	10	11	1

1	11	5	21	1

If it (a) .... on New Year's Day, it will be a wet year.

It if (b) .... on New Year's Day, it will be a (c) .... year.

If you have (d) .... luck on New Year's Day, you will be lucky all (e) ....

If you use a (f) .... or scissors on New Year's Day, you will (g) .... away all your luck for the year.

If you say (h) .... words like (i) .... or *accident* on New Year's Day, you will have an unlucky year.

If you say good words like *wealth* or (j) .... on New Year's Day, you will have a good year.

If you give children (k) .... on New Year's Day, they will have a lucky year.

If you wear the colour (l) .... on New Year's Day, you will have a lucky year.

Now use the same code to solve these words. These are all things you can see at Chinese New Year. Then write the correct word under each picture.

9	10	18	2

17	10	5	11

13	9	19	3

18	7	9	13	1

13	9	7	12	5	11

6	5	1	16	2	9

20	19	13	13	4	7

17	7	11	16	2	9	11

13	19	3	6	17	10	11	12	1

15	10	9	2	18	9	7	18	14	2	9	1

1 ....

2 ....

3 ....

4 ....

5 ....

6 ....

7 ....

8 ....

9 ....

10 ....

Burns Night Quiz

How much do you know about Burns Night?
Do the quiz with a friend. Take turns to ask the questions. Start at number one.
When you know the answers, you can write a story about Burns Night.

one
Is Burns Night an English or a Scottish festival?

English
(go to 15)

Scottish
(go to 6)

two
Wrong.

Go back to 14 and try again.

three
Correct.

Go to 20.

four
Wrong.

Go back to 11 and try again.

five
Wrong.

Go back to 16 and try again.

six
Correct.
Burns Night is the birthday of Robert Burns. When was he born?

25 January 1759
(go to 19)

25 August 1959
(go to 13)

seven
Wrong.

Go back to 9 and try again.

eight
Correct.
When do people celebrate Burns Night?

in the morning
(go to 18)

in the evening
(go to 14)

nine
Correct.
What do men wear on Burns Night?

a kilt
(go to 16)

a big hat
(go to 7)

ten
Wrong.

Go back to 19 and try again.

eleven
Correct.
What do people eat with haggis?

peas and carrots
(go to 4)

potatoes and turnips
(go to 17)

twelve
Wrong.

Go back to 17 and try again.

thirteen
Wrong.

Go back to 6 and try again.

fourteen
Correct.
On Burns Night people eat haggis. What is haggis?

a pie made of salmon and eggs
(go to 2)

a pudding made of meat, oats and spices
(go to 11)

fifteen
Wrong.

Go back to 1 and try again.

sixteen
Correct.
After the Burns dinner there is a big dance. What is it called?

a waltz
(go to 5)

a ceilidh
(go to 3)

seventeen
Correct.
Which musical instrument do people play on Burns Night?

the bagpipes
(go to 9)

the flute
(go to 12)

eighteen
Wrong.

Go back to 8 and try again.

nineteen
Correct.
Who is Robert Burns?

He is a famous poet.
(go to 8)

He is a famous dancer.
(go to 10)

twenty
Finish
Well done!
You know a lot about Burns Night.

Poem

Robert Burns wrote all his poems and songs in Scottish dialect.
Scottish people read his poem 'To a Haggis' on Burns Night and
they sing his song 'Auld Lang Syne' on New Year's Eve.

Here is a poem that you could write in a Valentine's card. A lot of the words are old Scottish words.
What do these words mean in modern English? Find the words in the box.

all	for a short time	girl	go	goodbye	melody	of
played	pretty	though	with	you	you are so beautiful	

My Love is Like a Red Red Rose

My love is like a red, red rose
That's newly sprung in June;
My love is like the (1) **melodie**
That's sweetly (2) **play'd** in tune.

(3) **So fair art thou**, my (4) **bonnie** (5) **lass**,
So deep in love am I:
And I will love (6) **thee** still, my dear,
Till (7) **a'** the seas (8) **gang** dry.

Till a' the seas gang dry, my dear,
And the rocks melt (9) **wi'** the sun:
And I will love thee still, my dear,
While the sands (10) **o'** life shall run.

And (11) **fare thee weel**, my only love,
And fare thee weel (12) **awhile**!
And I will come again, my love,
(13) **Tho'** it were ten thousand mile.

Find the picture that goes with each verse of the poem.

Valentine's Cards

On the 14th of February, people send a Valentine's card to the girl or boy they like.
Sometimes people write a poem, too.

Look at these poems and fill in each gap with an adjective from the box. Remember that the poems must rhyme.

bright   busy   cheeky   clever   fair   funny   great   mean   sweet

1
I like a girl
called Nicky
She's confid**e**nt and

....

2
I like a boy
calle**d** Dean
Because he's never

....

3
Please **b**e my
girlfriend, Claire.
I **l**ike you because
yo**u**'re always

....

4
My darling Pet**e**
You're very

....

5
Please be my
girlfriend, Lizzie.
Don't **s**ay that
you're too

....

6
This poem's
for a boy called
Andre**w** Knight.
I like you becaus**e**
you're kind and

....

7
Do you like m**e**,
Kate?
I **t**hink you're

....

8
You're much
sweeter than hone**y**
And you're als**o** very

....

9
I love you, Trevor
Beca**u**se you're

....

This is a traditional Valentine's poem.
Take the **bold** letters from the poems
above and make four new words.
Write the words in the gaps.

Roses are ....
Violets are ....
Sugar is ....
And so are ....

Computer Dating

These people are going to a Valentine's party. The party is for people who are looking for a girlfriend or boyfriend. They all have to fill in a form, then the computer finds their ideal partner. When they go to the party, they meet the person recommended by the computer.

The computer chooses people who have two likes and two dislikes the same. Ideally the two people should be the same age.

Read the forms that the eight people have filled in. Then complete the computer reports. Find the best partner for everybody.

Name: Anna Walters
Age: 15   Male ☐ Female ☑
Likes and dislikes:
tick three things you like doing and cross three things you don't like doing.
☒ watching TV/videos
☐ going to the cinema
☒ shopping
☑ listening to music
☑ playing sports
☒ playing computer games
☑ reading
☐ drawing/painting/making things

Name: Ben Taylor
Age: 15   Male ☑ Female ☐
Likes and dislikes:
tick three things you like doing and cross three things you don't like doing.
☐ watching TV/videos
☑ going to the cinema
☑ shopping
☒ listening to music
☒ playing sports
☐ playing computer games
☒ reading
☑ drawing/painting/making things

Name: Curtis Jackson
Age: 15   Male ☑ Female ☐
Likes and dislikes:
tick three things you like doing and cross three things you don't like doing.
☑ watching TV/videos
☐ going to the cinema
☒ shopping
☑ listening to music
☐ playing sports
☒ playing computer games
☑ reading
☒ drawing/painting/making things

Name: Vicky Bradshaw
Age: 16   Male ☐ Female ☑
Likes and dislikes:
tick three things you like doing and cross three things you don't like doing.
☒ watching TV/videos
☑ going to the cinema
☐ shopping
☒ listening to music
☑ playing sports
☐ playing computer games
☒ reading
☑ drawing/painting/making things

Name: Darren Wallis
Age: 16   Male ☑ Female ☐
Likes and dislikes:
tick three things you like doing and cross three things you don't like doing.
☑ watching TV/videos
☒ going to the cinema
☑ shopping
☐ listening to music
☒ playing sports
☑ playing computer games
☐ reading
☒ drawing/painting/making things

Name: Amy Callaghan
Age: 16   Male ☐ Female ☑
Likes and dislikes:
tick three things you like doing and cross three things you don't like doing.
☑ watching TV/videos
☒ going to the cinema
☒ shopping
☑ listening to music
☐ playing sports
☑ playing computer games
☐ reading
☒ drawing/painting/making things

Name: Nick Short
Age: 16   Male ☑ Female ☐
Likes and dislikes:
tick three things you like doing and cross three things you don't like doing.
☒ watching TV/videos
☑ going to the cinema
☐ shopping
☒ listening to music
☑ playing sports
☒ playing computer games
☑ reading
☐ drawing/painting/making things

Name: Gemma Theakston
Age: 15   Male ☐ Female ☑
Likes and dislikes:
tick three things you like doing and cross three things you don't like doing.
☐ watching TV/videos
☒ going to the cinema
☑ shopping
☐ listening to music
☒ playing sports
☑ playing computer games
☒ reading
☑ drawing/painting/making things

Anna Walters Neither Darren nor Ben is suitable for you. Your ideal partner is Curtis.

Ben Taylor Either .... or .... is suitable for you. Your ideal partner is ....

Amy Callaghan Neither .... nor .... is suitable for you. Your ideal partner is ....

Nick Short Neither .... nor .... is suitable for you. Your ideal partner is ....

Gemma Theakston Either .... or .... is suitable for you. Your ideal partner is ....

Curtis Jackson Either .... or .... is suitable for you. Your ideal partner is ....

Vicky Bradshaw Neither .... nor .... is suitable for you. Your ideal partner is ....

Darren Willis Either .... or .... is suitable for you. Your ideal partner is ....

The Story of Valentine's Day

Read the story of Valentine's Day. Choose the correct word to go in each gap and write it in the heart.
When you have finished you will find the names of two famous lovers.

baby	books	boyfriend	boys	cards	February	festival	holidays
husband	in	Juno	kissed	loved	men	Saturday	on	people	poems
post	sofa	stories	take	teddy	times	wall	weeks	women	Vishnu

In Roman times people celebrated a festival of love in the month of
1 .... The festival was called Lupercalia. It was the festival of
the Roman gods Pan and **2** .... Young men and young
3 .... played games to find a wife or a **4** ....

In early Christian **5** .... St Valentine was a holy man.
He was killed for his beliefs. Before he died he wrote a message on
the prison **6** .... The message was for the woman he
7 .... and he signed the message 'Your Valentine'.

The feast day of St Valentine is the fourteenth of February.
St Valentine's Day became the **8** .... of lovers.
Young men wrote **9** .... to give to young women.
If they were no good at writing poetry, they copied one from a
book. Girls made cards to give to the young **10** ....
The sender of the card was a secret. People never signed the cards.

In the nineteenth century, the postal
service started. Now people could
11 .... their
Valentine's cards.

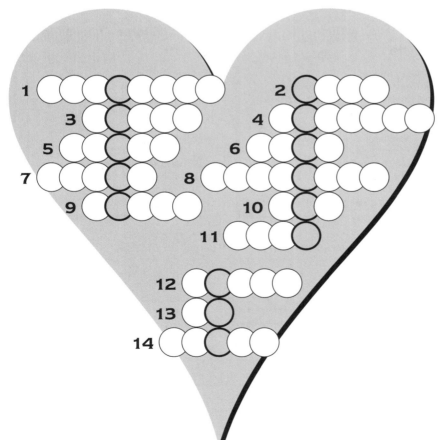

1
3
5
7
9
11
2
4
6
8
10
12
13
14

Today you can buy lots of
12 .... and presents
to send **13** ....
Valentine's Day. How about a cute
14 .... bear, a heart-
shaped balloon or twelve red roses?

Pancake Fillings

**Pancake Day is the day before Lent. It is forty days before Easter.
In Britain, people eat pancakes. These are made of eggs, flour and milk.
It is traditional to eat pancakes with lemon juice and sugar. This is delicious,
but now lots of other pancake fillings are popular, too.**

Look at the ingredients for pancake fillings. Write the correct word under each picture.
Then look at the number in the box. Count the number of letters in the word and write the letter.
Find another name for Pancake Day.

For example, the first picture is **cheese**. The fifth letter of cheese is **S**.

5	1	3	4	2	1
chee**s**e					

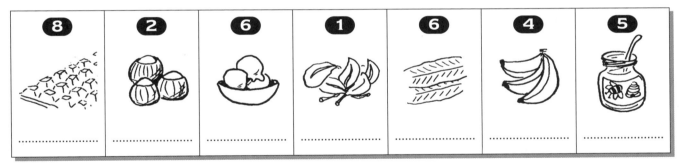

8	2	6	1	6	4	5

avocado
bananas
<u>cheese</u>
chocolate
eggs
ham
honey
ice-cream
nuts
onion
smoked salmon
spinach
strawberries

Write the letters here.

S __ __ __ __ __

__ __ __ __ __ __

Pancake Tossing Competition

**In many places in Britain, there are pancake tossing competitions on Pancake Day.
The person who cooks and tosses the most pancakes in ten minutes wins.**

Kieran, Holly, Martin, Jason and Tiffany are in a pancake tossing competition.
How many pancakes does each person toss in ten minutes?
Write the numbers on the pancakes, then answer the questions.

▲ = one pancake   ● = two pancakes   ■ = three pancakes   ★ = four pancakes

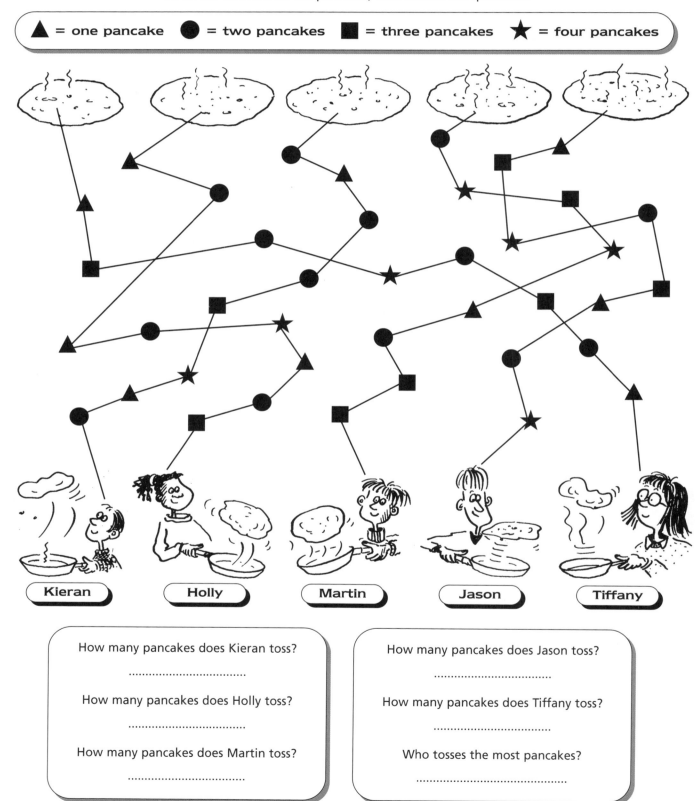

Kieran   Holly   Martin   Jason   Tiffany

How many pancakes does Kieran toss?

....

How many pancakes does Holly toss?

....

How many pancakes does Martin toss?

....

How many pancakes does Jason toss?

....

How many pancakes does Tiffany toss?

....

Who tosses the most pancakes?

....

Lent

Pancake Day is the day before Lent. Lent is the period of forty days before Easter.
Many Christians give up something they enjoy doing for Lent.

Look at the pictures. These people are all going to give up these things for Lent.
Write what they are giving up in the grid. Use the words in the box.
The last letter of each thing is the first letter of the next word.

cinema sweets the eating going buying school to eating going listening cake clothes theatre singing going to the to acting music to cycling swimming

I'd better give up ...

I should give up ...

I should give up ...

I should give up ...

I'd better give up ...

I should give up ...

I'd better give up ...

I'd better give up ...

I should give up ...

I'd better give up ...

I should give up ...

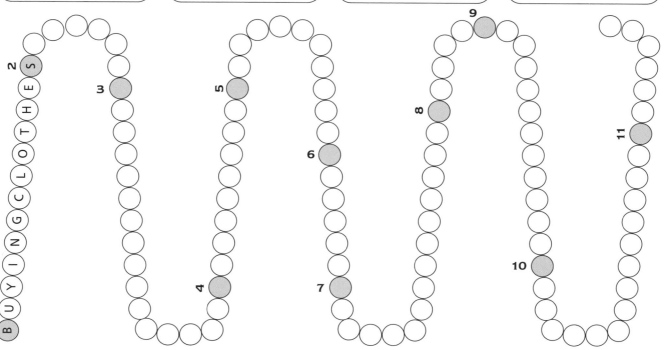

One of the people is only joking about what they're going to give up. Which person is it?

Number .... is joking.

Animal Photographs

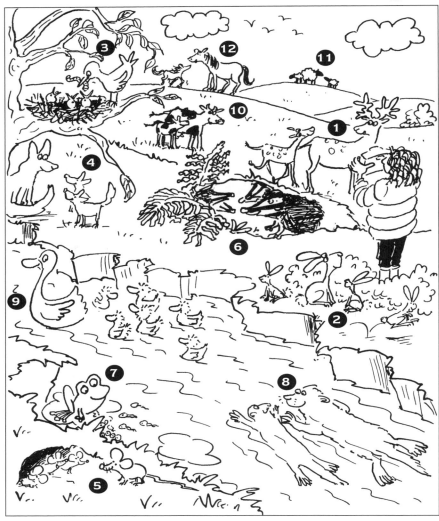

In the Spring there are lots of baby animals. Amy is taking photos of the animals. She is not a very good photographer. Look at Amy's photos.
Write the names of the adult animals. Write the names of the baby animals.

	adult	babies
1	*deer*	*fawn*
2		
3		
4		
5		
6		
7		
8		
9		
10		
11		
12		

This is a bird and some chicks.

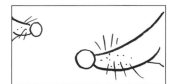

This is a mouse and some baby mice.

This is a horse and a foal.

This is an otter and an otter cub.

This is a frog and lots of tadpoles.

This is a rabbit and some baby rabbits.

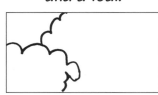

This is a sheep and some lambs.

This is a deer and a fawn.

This is a duck and some ducklings.

This is a cow and a calf.

This is a badger and some badger cubs.

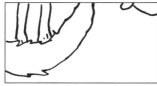

This is a fox and some fox cubs.

Spring Festivals

Look at the Spring flowers. Find the pairs that are exactly the same to make sentences.

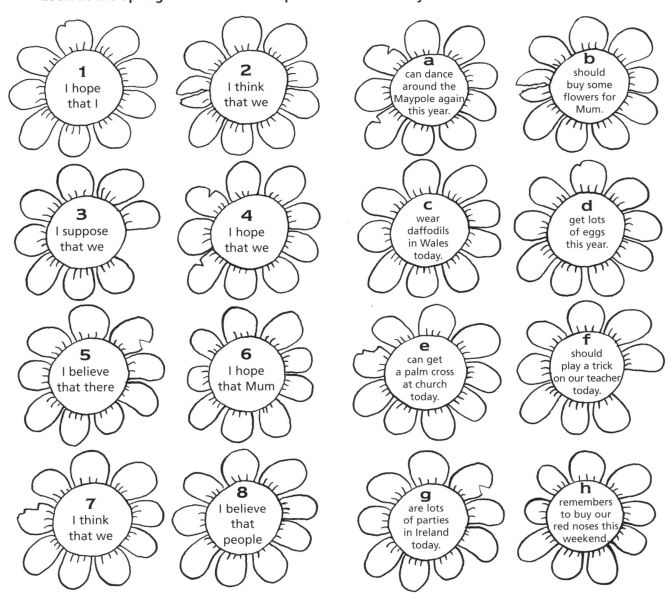

1 I hope that I

2 I think that we

a can dance around the Maypole again this year.

b should buy some flowers for Mum.

3 I suppose that we

4 I hope that we

c wear daffodils in Wales today.

d get lots of eggs this year.

5 I believe that there

6 I hope that Mum

e can get a palm cross at church today.

f should play a trick on our teacher today.

7 I think that we

8 I believe that people

g are lots of parties in Ireland today.

h remembers to buy our red noses this weekend.

Now write the correct festival in each flower.

1   **2**   **3**   **4**

5   **6**   **7**   **8**

Easter
St David's Day
April Fool's Day
Palm Sunday
Comic Relief
St Patrick's Day
May Day
Mother's Day

Saints' Names

Who are the patron saints of Scotland, Wales, Ireland and England?
Look at the towns on the map. Make a name from the **bold** letters in each country.
Read the information about each saint's day. Write the correct name in the sentences.

The patron saint of Scotland
is St ....
St ....'s Day is on
the 30th of November.
On St ....'s Day
Scottish people wear a thistle.

The patron saint of Ireland is
St ....
St ....'s Day is on
the 17th of March.
On St ....'s Day
Irish people wear a shamrock.

INVE**R**NESS

ABERDEEN

Scotland

DUND**E**E

EDI**N**BURGH

GLASGO**W**

**Northern
Ireland**

LE**T**TERKENNY
LONDON-DE**R**RY
BELF**A**ST

DUMFRIES

PORTAFER**R**Y

**Republic
of Ireland**

LIVE**R**POOL

L**E**EDS
MANCH**E**STER

DUBL**I**N

LLAN**D**UDNO

England

KIL**K**ENNY

Wales

BIRMIN**G**HAM

CORK

CARD**I**GAN

MILFORD
HA**V**EN

SW**A**NSEA

LO**N**DON

CAR**D**I**F**F

BRI**G**HTON

The patron saint of Wales is
St ....
St ....'s Day is on
the 1st of March.
On St ....'s Day
Welsh people wear a daffodil.

The patron saint of England is
St ....
St ....'s Day is on
the 23rd of April.
On St ....'s Day
English people wear a red rose.

0   200

km

St Patrick's Day Postcard

**St Patrick is the patron saint of Ireland. St Patrick's Day is the 17th of March.
It is a big festival in Ireland.**

Tara is on holiday in Ireland. She is writing a postcard to her friend. Read the postcard and find the correct verbs to go in the spaces. Change the verbs to the correct tense and write them in the grid.

to buy
to eat
to find
to be
to listen
to watch

Dear Anil,
I'm having a lovely holiday in Dublin.
Today is St Patrick's Day. I've done lots
of nice things.
I've (1) .... out a lot about
Irish traditions.
I've (2) .... to some
Irish music.
I've (3) .... to the
St Patrick's Day parade.
I've (4) .... some Irish stew.
I've (5) .... some traditional
Irish dancing.
I've (6) .... a present for you.
See you soon.
Lots of love,
Tara

Anil Gupta
27 Drakefield Road
London
N16 7JD

Write the words in the grid and find the Irish word for festival.

1
2
3
4
5
6

The Irish word for festival is

....

(Irish pronunciation is different from
English pronunciation.
Say this word so it rhymes with 'car'.)

Welsh and English

St David's Day is on the 1st of March. It is an important festival in Wales.
Welsh people celebrate their country and their language.

In Wales many people speak two languages: Welsh and English.

The road signs are in both languages.

Can you write the English names on the road sign?

Read the clues and find the English words for these Welsh words. Write the English words in the grids. The words are at the bottom of the page.

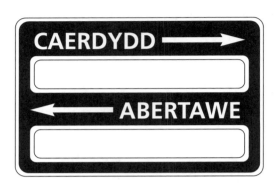

CAERDYDD →

← ABERTAWE

CAERDYDD

1 Mawrth
St David's Day is on the 1st of ...

2 Cymru
People speak Welsh in this country.

3 rygbi
This sport is very popular in Wales.

4 Dewy
This is the name of the patron saint of Wales.

5 pedwar ugain
Wales is a very small country. It is only ... kilometres wide.

6 eisteddfod
This is a celebration.

7 cenhinen Bedr
People wear this flower on St David's Day.

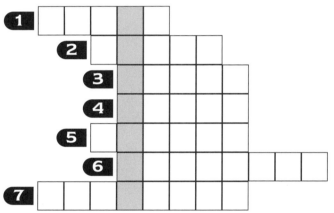

ABERTAWE

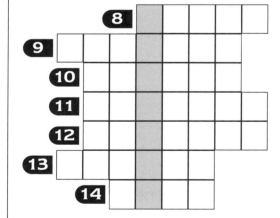

8 defaid
There are lots of these animals in Wales.

9 Yr Wyddfa
This is the tallest mountain in Wales.

10 draig
This animal is the symbol of Wales.

11 canu
Lots of Welsh people sing in choirs. They love ...

12 cestyll
There are lots of these old buildings in Wales.

13 caws
There are lots of delicious types of this food in Wales.

14 glawio
This weather is very common in Wales.

RAIN   SHEEP   WALES   DAVID   RUGBY

MARCH   CHEESE   DRAGON   EIGHTY   SNOWDON

CASTLES   SINGING   DAFFODIL   FESTIVAL

Making Words

Mother's Day is on a Sunday. It is three weeks before Easter. On Mother's Day children give presents, flowers and cards to their mothers. An old name for Mother's Day is Mothering Sunday.

How many words can you make from the letters in Mothering Sunday?

M O T H E R I N G   S U N D A Y

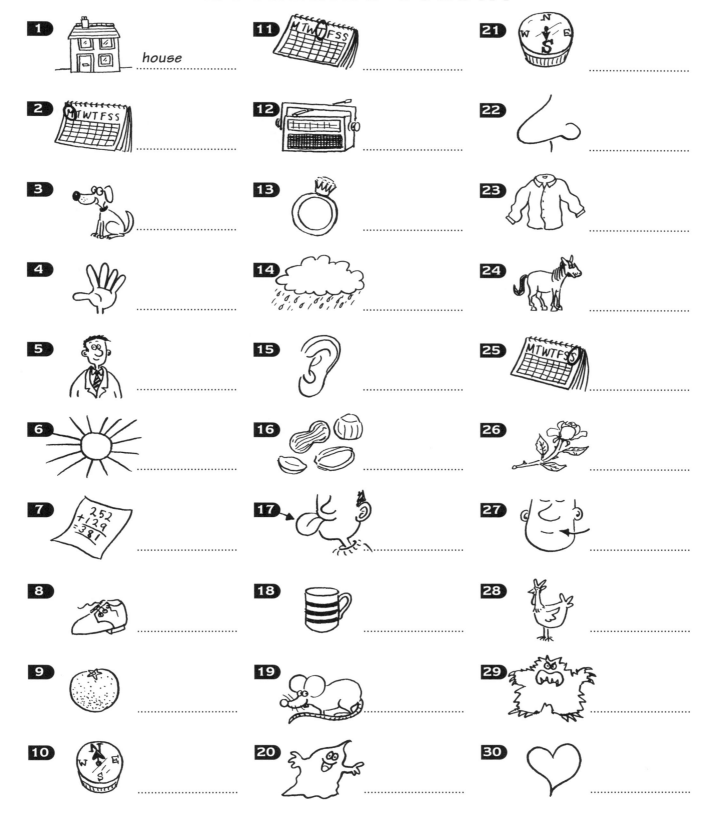

1 house ....

2 ....

3 ....

4 ....

5 ....

6 ....

7 ....

8 ....

9 ....

10 ....

11 ....

12 ....

13 ....

14 ....

15 ....

16 ....

17 ....

18 ....

19 ....

20 ....

21 ....

22 ....

23 ....

24 ....

25 ....

26 ....

27 ....

28 ....

29 ....

30 ....

Mother's Day Traditions

Work out the code and write the words in the crossword.
Each letter has a number. There are four letters already in the crossword to help you.

M is number 9.
O is number 7.
H is number 12.
L is number 4.

First write all the Ms, Os, Hs and Ls.
Then work out the numbers of all the other letters.

A	N
B	O̸
C	P
D	Q
E	R
F	S
G	T
H̶	U
I	V
J	W
K	X
L̶	Y
M̶	Z

Crossword grid:

Row 1: 10, 9, ■, 12, 7, 9, 15, ■, 26, ■, 17, ■
Row 2: ■, 10, ■, 7, ■, 8, ■, 5, 16, 1, 10, 3
Row 3: 1, 2, 3, 4 (L), 5, ■, ■, ■, 2, ■, 4, ■
Row 4: ■, 11, ■, 2, ■, 15, ■, 13, 10, 14, 15, ■
Row 5: 16, 5, 15, 11, ■, 4, 7, 7, 14, ■, ■, ■
Row 6: 21, ■, ■, 10, 1, 15, ■, ■, 4, 7, 19, 5
Row 7: ■, 9, 10, 8, ■, 18, 15, 3, 8, ■, ■, ■
Row 8: ■, 10, 19, ■, 17, 15, ■, ■, ■, 7, 23, 23
Row 9: 21, 3, 15, 5, 15, 20, 19, 5, ■, ■, 4, ■
Row 10: ■, 22, ■, ■, 20, ■, ■, ■, 23, 3, 7, 9
Row 11: 18, 2, 5, 2, 19, ■, 9 (M), ■, 2, ■, 17, ■
Row 12: ■, 21, ■, ■, ■, 25, 7 (O), 16, 3, 20, 15, 8
Row 13: 12, 10, 3, 11, ■, ■, 19, ■, 5, ■, 3, ■
Row 14: 10, 20, ■, ■, 6, ■, 12 (H), 10, 19, ■, 5, 7
Row 15: 11, ■, ■, 16, ■, 15, ■, ■, ■, 7, ■, 16
Row 16: ■, 9, 2, 24, 19, 16, 3, 15, ■, 20, 7, 19

1	2	3	4	5	6	7	8	9	10	11	12	13
			L			O		M			H	

14	15	16	17	18	19	20	21	22	23	24	25	26

Mother's Day Traditions
Read about Mother's Day today and in the past.
Choose words from the crossword to fill the gaps in the story. Use each word only once.

A

Mother's Day is in (a) .... in many countries, but in Britain it is in March, three weeks before

Easter. Children give cards and (b)........................... to their mothers. They say thank you for all the things

their mothers do for them.

In the nineteenth century many young (c).......................... went away (d)........................... home. They

(e)........................... to work as (f)........................... for rich people. They worked very (g)...........................

They did (h)........................... get (i)........................... much time (j)........................... , (k)...........................

Mothering Sunday was a (l)........................... The maids were allowed to go (m)........................... to

(n)........................... their mothers. They (o)........................... to make a special cake for their mothers.

It was made of a (p)........................... of fruit, spices and (q)........................... and it was decorated with

(r)...........................

B

(a)...........................name is Janet. I (b)........................... a maid. I

(c)........................... went to be a maid at the (d)........................... of

(e)........................... Today I am going to visit my (f)...........................

This morning I (g)........................... to get (h)........................... at

four o'clock. I put (i)........................... my best dress and my best

(j)........................... , then I (k)........................... my breakfast

(l)........................... half past four. I am going (m)...........................

at five o'clock. It is a long (n)........................... to my mother's house

(o)........................... I will have to (p)........................... very

(q)........................... I have got (r)........................... of presents for my

mother. I've got a (s)........................... and some honey. On the way

home I am going to (t)........................... for some

(u)........................... to pick.

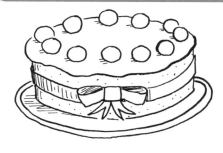

**People still make special cakes for Mother's Day.
Use the same code as in the crossword to find the
name of the cake.**

5	2	9	20	15	4

13	10	14	15

What Colour Is It?

Comic Relief is in March once every two years.
People do funny things and make money for charity.
Find something that people wear for Comic Relief.

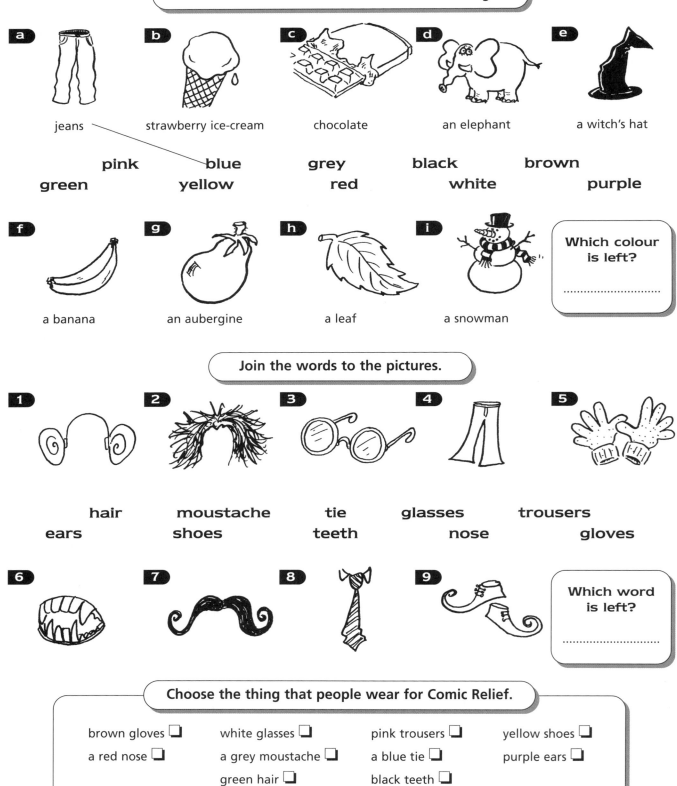

What colour is it? Join the colours to the things.

a jeans

b strawberry ice-cream

c chocolate

d an elephant

e a witch's hat

pink   blue   grey   black   brown

green   yellow   red   white   purple

f a banana

g an aubergine

h a leaf

i a snowman

Which colour is left?

....

Join the words to the pictures.

1   **2**   **3**   **4**   **5**

hair   moustache   tie   glasses   trousers

ears   shoes   teeth   nose   gloves

6   **7**   **8**   **9**

Which word is left?

....

Choose the thing that people wear for Comic Relief.

brown gloves ❑   white glasses ❑   pink trousers ❑   yellow shoes ❑

a red nose ❑   a grey moustache ❑   a blue tie ❑   purple ears ❑

green hair ❑   black teeth ❑

New School Rules

Comic Relief is in March every two years. Another name for Comic Relief is Red Nose Day. People wear red noses and do funny things to make money for charity.

At Alan's school, the students are writing funny rules for Comic Relief.

On Red Nose Day they must obey the funny rules.

Read the rules. Which are the real school rules and which are the rules for Red Nose Day? Tick the Red Nose Day rules.

SCHOOL RULES

1. You must be polite to your teachers.
2. You must arrive at school on time.
3. You must wear a red nose.
4. You must sing in lessons.
5. You must not chew chewing-gum.
6. You must be quiet in the corridor.
7. You must work hard in lessons.
8. You must throw wet sponges at your teacher.
9. You must not fight.
10. You must dance in the corridor.
11. You must not smoke.
12. You must laugh when your teacher speaks.
13. You must stand on your head in assembly.
14. You must not run in the corridor.
15. You must wear school uniform.
16. You must do your homework.
17. You must wear your clothes back-to-front.
18. You must write with a pink pen.
19. You must not wear make-up at school.

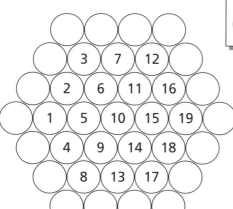

Now colour the red noses with the same numbers as the Red Nose Day rules. What is the picture?

a a flower ☐

b a face ☐

c a star ☐

Charity Projects

Comic Relief happens every two years in March.
There are lots of humorous events all over the UK to raise money for charity projects.
Every year Comic Relief makes millions of pounds for projects in the UK and in Africa.

These people all need money from Comic Relief to help people where they live.
Read about the projects and complete the phrasal verbs. Choose the correct word from the box.

away	into	off	on	out	out	over	through	up	up

1 There is no water supply in my village. We have to collect water from the stream. When the stream dries .... we have to walk 20 kilometres to find water. We want to build a well in the village.

2 I live in a big city and there are lots of young homeless people. We want to build a hostel to help the young people get .... the streets and start a new life.

3 People in my town are very poor. Many people are born with disabilities. We want to build a special school so that disabled children can grow .... to be independent and happy.

4 We want to help children and teenagers who are the victims of abuse. We want to start a counselling service to help people get .... their bad experiences.

5 I live on a big council estate. There is nothing for young people to do. A lot of teenagers get .... drugs and crime. We want to build a sports centre so that young people have something positive to do.

6 My country is going .... some terrible times. There is a war and lots of people have lost their homes. We want to help people to build new homes.

7 It is very difficult for disabled people to go .... in my town. We can't be as independent as we would like to be. The buses aren't adapted for wheelchairs. We want to buy a special bus so that people in wheelchairs can get .... the bus.

8 Where I live HIV and AIDS are big problems. We want to employ a teacher so that people can find .... how to prevent AIDS.

9 In my town there is a lot of unemployment. Most families don't have enough money to go .... on holiday. We want to provide adventure holidays for children and teenagers.

Who Is the Fool?

April Fool's Day is on the 1st of April.
A fool is a silly person.

On April Fool's Day people play tricks
on their family and friends.

> If you play a trick before 12 o'clock
> you can say 'April Fool'.
>
> If you play a trick after 12 o'clock
> you are the fool.

These people are all playing tricks. Look at the clocks and write the times under the pictures.
Who is the fool in each picture?

1

'There's a spider in your hair.'

Dean Esther

What time is it?
It's nine o'clock.

Who is the fool?
Esther

2

Arti Jason

What time is it?
....

Who is the fool?
....

3

Simon 'Who's there?' Vicky

What time is it?
....

Who is the fool?
....

4

I'M FOOL

Anna Kerry

What time is it?
....

Who is the fool?
....

5

Miss O'Donnell Jack

What time is it?
....

Who is the fool?
....

6

'Look. I'm bleeding!'

KETCHUP

Edward Sanjay

What time is it?
....

Who is the fool?
....

7

'Why is your hair green?'

Sonia Tina

What time is it?
....

Who is the fool?
....

8

Kim 'Would you like a sweet?' 'Yes, please.' Joseph

What time is it?
....

Who is the fool?
....

Are You an April Fool?

April Fool's Day is on the 1st of April. It isn't a holiday but it is a day for playing tricks. Do you like playing tricks?

Seven teenagers are talking about tricks they have played on April Fool's Day. Choose the correct tense of each verb and write it in the gap in the sentence.

Then decide what you think about each trick. Tick the box.

Ask your teacher for the analysis.

1 Jamie

I put a cup of water on top of the kitchen door. I said to my dad that I .... to talk to him in the kitchen. When he opened the door the water fell on him. He got very wet.

want / wanted

What do you think of this trick?
a It's funny. ☐
b It's silly. ☐
c It's unkind. ☐

2 Kathryn

I said to my mum that somebody .... the doorbell. When she came there was nobody there.

to ring / was ringing

What do you think of this trick?
a It's funny. ☐
b It's silly. ☐
c It's unkind. ☐

3 Mike

I told my little sister that it .... outside. She looked out of the window but it wasn't snowing.

will snow / was snowing

What do you think of this trick?
a It's funny. ☐
b It's silly. ☐
c It's unkind. ☐

4 Paula

I told my big sister that a spider .... in her hair. She hates spiders so she started screaming.

crawls / was crawling

What do you think of this trick?
a It's funny. ☐
b It's silly. ☐
c It's unkind. ☐

5 Carl

I told my dad that there .... a fire in the living room. He came running into the room but there wasn't a fire.

was / is

What do you think of this trick?
a It's funny. ☐
b It's silly. ☐
c It's unkind. ☐

6 Leila

I said to my friend that I .... a present for her. When she opened it there was just a big stone in the box.

am buying / had bought

What do you think of this trick?
a It's funny. ☐
b It's silly. ☐
c It's unkind. ☐

7 Damon

I pushed over a chair to make a loud noise and I lay down on the floor. My brother heard the noise and came into the room. I said that I .... my leg. He wanted to call an ambulance.

have broken / had broken

What do you think of this trick?
a It's funny. ☐
b It's silly. ☐
c It's unkind. ☐

Easter Egg Hunt

Chocolate Easter eggs are popular in Britain.

Sometimes people hide Easter eggs and children look for them. There are eight Easter eggs in the garden. Read the clues and find the eggs. Write the position of each egg.

Start at the sundial.

1. Go south-east to some flowers.

7D ....

2. Go west to a bench.

....

3. Go south-east to a statue.

....

4. Go north to a swing.

....

5. Go south-west to a fountain.

....

6. Go north-west to a wheelbarrow.

....

7. Go east to a tree.

....

8. Go north to a statue.

....

Hot Cross Buns

Good Friday is the Friday before Easter Sunday. On Good Friday, Christians remember when Jesus died on the cross. In Britain, hot cross buns are popular on Good Friday.

Look at the pictures and read the anagrams. Read the recipe and find the verbs. Write the verb under each picture. Match the pictures and the instructions.

Ingredients

For the yeast mixture:
1 tablespoon dried yeast
1 teaspoon sugar
50 millilitres milk
150 millilitres warm water
100 grams flour

For the buns:
350 grams flour
1 teaspoon salt
1 teaspoon mixed spice
1 teaspoon cinnamon
1 teaspoon nutmeg
50 grams sugar
50 grams butter
1 egg
25 grams currants
40 grams mixed peel

1. Pour the warm milk and the warm water into a bowl. ☐

2. Add the sugar, yeast and 100 grams of flour. Leave for 20 to 30 minutes in a warm place. ☐

3. Sift 350 grams of flour, 50 grams of sugar, the salt, mixed spice, cinnamon and nutmeg. ☐

4. Melt the butter in a saucepan. *a*

5. Beat the egg. Add the butter and the egg to the yeast mixture. Add the flour mixture, the currants and the mixed peel. ☐

6. Stir the mixture well. ☐

7. Knead the dough with your hands for 10 minutes. ☐

8. Divide the dough into 12 pieces. ☐

9. Place the buns on a baking tray. ☐

10. Cover the buns with a tea towel. Leave in a warm place for 45 minutes. ☐

11. Cut a cross on the top of each bun with a knife. ☐

12. Put the buns in the oven (190°C). Bake for 15 to 20 minutes. ☐

LEMT *melt* ....

DANKE ....

TABE ....

ROPU ....

TRIS ....

VIDEID ....

DAD ....

UPT ....

TIFS ....

RECOV ....

TUC ....

CALPE ....

Easter Words
Can you make these Easter words by changing letters each time?
Read the clues to help you find the words.

1 The Sunday before Easter is called Palm Sunday. Christians go to church and they receive a palm cross. Holy Week is the week before Easter. During Holy Week people remember the week before Jesus died.

Change **one** letter each time to make PALM into HOLY.

P A L M

P A L E light-coloured

_ A L E the opposite of female

_ _ _ _ a small black animal that lives underground

_ _ _ _ There's a ... in my school bag and all my pens have fallen out.

H O L Y

2 Good Friday is at the end of Holy Week. On Good Friday people remember the day when Jesus died on the cross.

Change **one** letter each time to make HOLY into GOOD.

H O L Y

H O L D Do you want to ... the baby in your arms?

_ _ _ _ the opposite of *hot*

_ _ _ _ the past tense of *to tell*

_ _ _ _ an expensive metal

G O O D

3 Easter Sunday is the Sunday after Good Friday. Christians believe that Jesus rose from the dead on Easter Sunday.

Change **two** letters each time to change EASTER into SUNDAY.

E A S T E R

_ _ _ _ _ _ brother and ...

_ _ _ _ _ _ You can run ... than me.

_ _ _ _ _ _ I am quite fit but you do more sport so you are ... than me.

_ _ _ _ _ _ the opposite of *colder*

_ _ _ _ _ _ 'I'm sorry I forgot your birthday.' 'Don't worry. It doesn't ... '

_ _ _ _ _ _ crazier

_ _ _ _ _ _ more difficult

_ _ _ _ _ _ a German composer

_ _ _ _ _ _ a shoe for the summer

S U N D A Y

4 Hot cross buns are popular in Britain at Easter. They are bread buns with currants and spices. Easter eggs are also popular at Easter. Parents tell their children that the Easter Bunny (rabbit) brings the Easter eggs. In some countries in Europe the Easter Hare brings the eggs.

Change **one** letter each time to change BUNS into HARE.

B U N S On Good Friday, people eat special buns called hot cross ...

B A N S forbids

_ _ _ _ pop group

_ _ _ _ It's got four fingers and a thumb.

_ _ _ _ the opposite of *easy*

H A R E

Maypole Dancing

May Day is the first Monday in May. There is no school and most people don't go to work. Maypole dancing is a tradition on May Day.

Look at the ribbons on the Maypole. Each ribbon describes one of the children dancing. But there are some extra letters between the words. The extra letters spell the name of the person.

Read the descriptions and find the letters. Write the names next to the people.

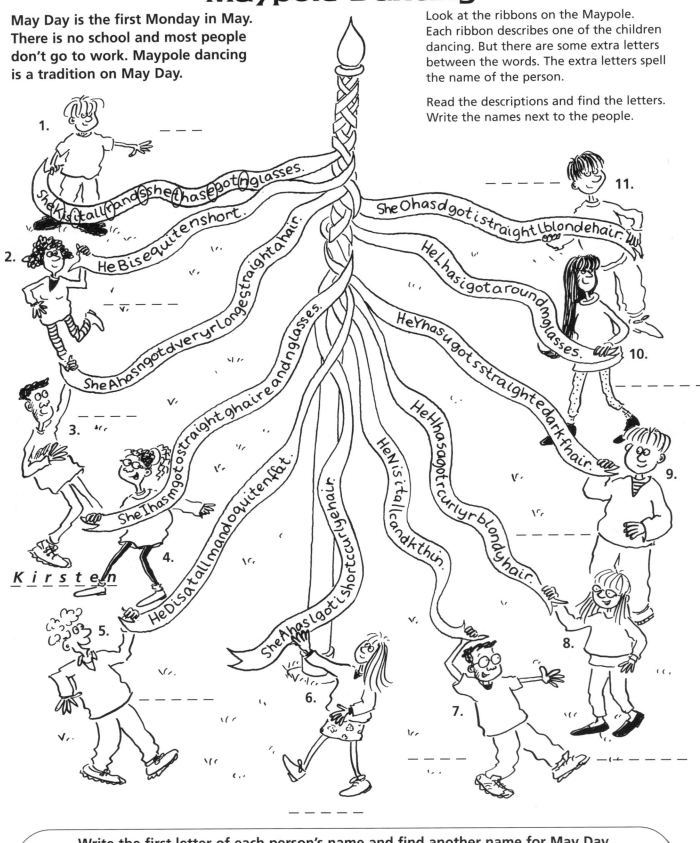

1. _ _ _ _

SheKisitallrandsshethaspotnglasses.

2. _ _ _ _

HeBisequitenshort.

SheAhasngotdveryrlongestraightahair.

3. _ _ _ _

SheIhasmgotostraightghaireandnglasses.

_K i r s t e n_

HeDisatallmandoquitenffat.

4. _ _ _ _

5. _ _ _ _

SheAhaslgotishortccurlyehair.

6. _ _ _ _

HeNisitallcandkthin.

7. _ _ _ _

HeHhasagotrcurlyrblondyhair.

8. _ _ _ _

9. _ _ _ _

HeYhasugotsstraightedarkfhair.

10. _ _ _ _

HeLhasigotaroundmglasses.

SheOhasdgotistraightlblondehair.

11. _ _ _ _

Write the first letter of each person's name and find another name for May Day.

_ _ _ K _ _ _ _ _ _ _
1 2 3 4   5 6 7 8 9 10 11

Word Spirals

**May Day is a very old festival. It used to be a pagan festival.
People danced and sang and they asked the gods to give them a good year.
Today celebrates the beginning of summer. Lots of people still dance on May Day.**

Here are two things that are traditional on May Day. Complete the word spirals.
All the words have got four letters. The last letter of each word is the first letter of the next word.

A

People dance around a Maypole on May Day. Can you complete the word spiral?

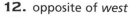

1. past simple of *to sell*
2. past simple of *to draw*
3. quite hot
4. plural of *mouse*
5. not difficult
6. my, his/her, ..., our, their
7. The first school ... is 'You must wear school uniform'
8. You hear with these
9. She ... that she likes swimming
10. You sit on this. It is bigger than a chair
11. I won't be ... to come to your party because I'm going on holiday
12. opposite of *west*
13. past simple of *to tell*
14. short name for *David*
15. You see with these
16. opposite of *go*

B

**In the Middle Ages, every girl in the village used to make one of these on May Day.
You can still see them in some places in England. What is it called?**

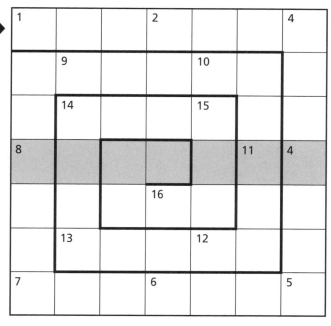

1. past simple of *to grow*
2. A bird uses this to fly
3. an expensive metal
4. You go into a room through this
5. It's on top of a house. It stops the rain coming in
6. past simple of *to fall*
7. How ... do we have to wait?
8. past simple of *to give*
9. She ... her lunch at one o'clock every day
10. Have you ... Dan? I'm looking for him
11. We ... some eggs to make the cake
12. Let's ... into the pool
13. a test
14. I'll ... you when you move house
15. past simple of *to sing*
16. opposite of *boy*

Theme Park Maze

In the Summer, lots of people go to theme parks.
Look at the symbols. Follow the directions and go to five rides.

★ = Turn left.　■ = Turn right.　▲ = Go straight on.

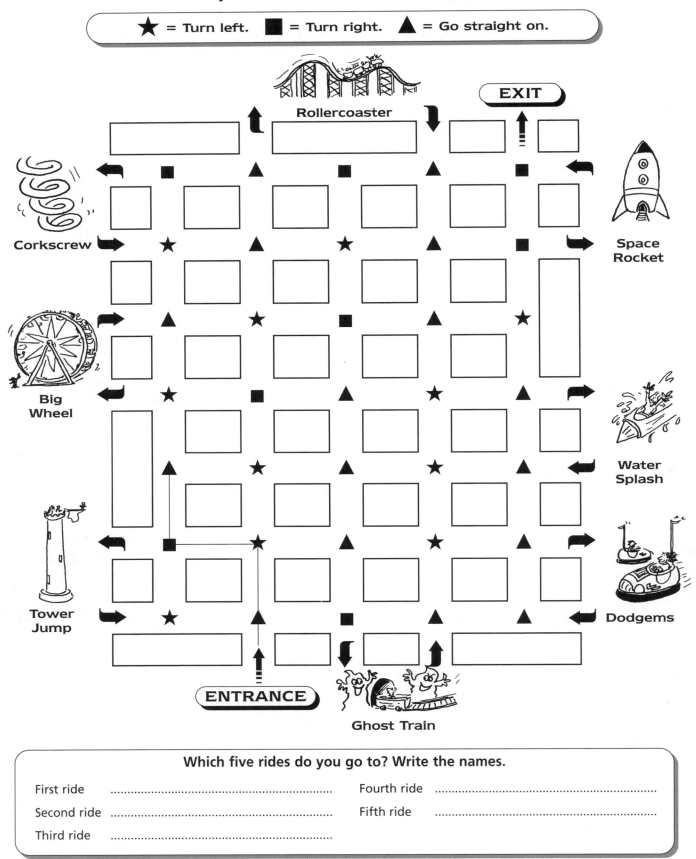

Which five rides do you go to? Write the names.

First ride ....

Second ride ....

Third ride ....

Fourth ride ....

Fifth ride ....

Rollercoaster

Summer is the time to go to the fun fair. Marcus is talking about the first time he went to a fair. Choose the words to fill the spaces in the story. Write the missing words in the roller coaster grid. The last letter of each word is the first letter of the next word.

I was seven years old and it was the first time I **24** *had* ever gone to a fair. It was **12**.......................... when we arrived and it was already **25**.......................... . It was like a **18**.......................... . I **20**.......................... believe that there were so many **16**.......................... to go on. There were lots of people – adults and **6**.......................... . Loud **19**.......................... was playing everywhere. First we went on the roller coaster. I had **15**.......................... **1**.......................... on a roller coaster before. I liked it, **23**.......................... it made me feel a bit **5**.......................... . I **22**.......................... go on the **13**.......................... **14**.......................... . I **9**.......................... II.......... because I was **7**.......................... . However, I **8**.......................... have a go at the darts. You had to **21**.......................... darts and score over 50. I had never **10**.......................... this game before, so I was **17**.......................... to find that I was very **3**.......................... at it. I **27**.......................... a teddy bear. My mum bought us some fizzy **4**.......................... . I didn't **26**.......................... what to do next. **2**.......................... else interested me, so we went home.

been	couldn't	dare	dark	did
didn't	dream	drinks	evening
ghost	good	had	kids	know
music	never	nothing	rides
scared	sick	surprised	though
throw	train	tried	won	wouldn't

Which Event?

It's sports day at Christine's school. Christine, Neelam, Gemma, Melanie and Bryony are competing. Each girl can only choose one event. Which event does each girl choose? Use the table to help you.

I'm good at the javelin and the high jump.
I'm bad at the 100 metres, the 800 metres and the long jump.

I'm good at the high jump, the 100 metres and the 800 metres.
I'm bad at the javelin and the long jump.

Christine

Neelam

I'm good at the long jump and the 800 metres.
I'm bad at the 100 metres, the high jump and the javelin.

Gemma

I'm only good at the 800 metres.
I'm bad at the long jump, the high jump, the 100 metres and the javelin.

I'm good at the 800 metres and the high jump.
I'm bad at the long jump, the 100 metres and the javelin.

Melanie

Bryony

	high jump	javelin	100 metres	800 metres	long jump
Christine					
Neelam					
Gemma					
Melanie					
Bryony					

Christine chooses the ....

Neelam chooses the ....

Gemma chooses the ....

Melanie chooses the ....

Bryony chooses the ....

Who's the Winner?

**Schools in Britain have a sports day before the summer holidays.
There are athletics events, such as races, high jump and long jump competitions.**

These pupils are in the 200 metres race.
Look at the picture and make a **compound adjective** to describe each person. Choose one word from each box.
Then look at the letters in the shaded squares to find out who wins the race.

1. Kate is
2. Jake is
3. Lucy is
4. Adam is
5. Beth is
6. Mark is
7. Arti is
8. Zach is

bad	headed
big	hearted
fun	humoured
good	loving
hard	sighted
kind	spirited
mean	tempered
short	working

Tombola

Lots of schools, churches and villages have a fête in the Summer.
There are things to buy, games and food. A popular game is the tombola.

Look at the tickets on the tombola prizes. Write the name of each prize under the correct person.
Write **nothing** if the person hasn't got a prize.

| some candles | a CD | a doll | a game | some perfume |
| a teddy bear | a Walkman | some wine | | |

a I've got number two hundred and eight.

....

b I've got number three hundred and fifty-two.

....

c I've got number seven hundred and thirty-three.

....

d I've got number four hundred and twenty-five.

....

e I've got number nine hundred and seventy-four.

....

f I've got number five hundred and twelve

....

g I've got number four hundred and fifty-two.

....

h I've got number three hundred and ninety-two.

....

i I've got number six hundred and forty-seven.

....

Which prize is left? **Write the ticket number in words.**

....

Prize Puzzle

At the Summer fête there are lots of games to play.
Look at the games at this fête. Fit the pieces into the jigsaw puzzle and make five sentences.
Write the names of the people in the picture.

Ben   John   Nick   Rick   Tom

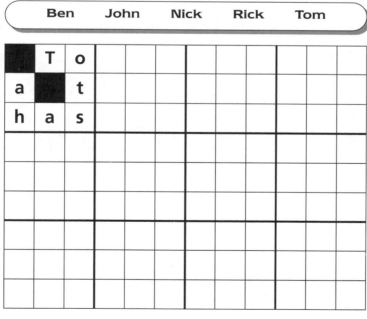

Father's Day Cards

Father's Day is the third Sunday in June. Children give cards and presents to their dads.
Which dad likes which hobby? Look at the maze and complete the sentences.

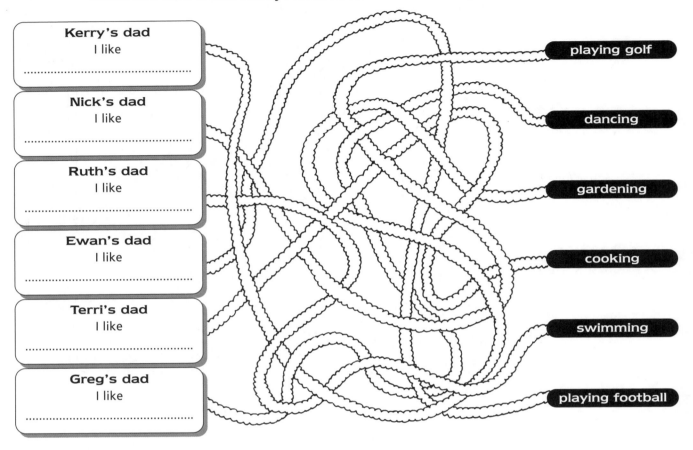

Kerry's dad
I like
....

Nick's dad
I like
....

Ruth's dad
I like
....

Ewan's dad
I like
....

Terri's dad
I like
....

Greg's dad
I like
....

playing golf

dancing

gardening

cooking

swimming

playing football

Which person buys which Father's Day card? Join the people and the cards.

1 Kerry   2 Nick   3 Ruth   4 Ewan   5 Terri   6 Greg

a   b   c   d   e   f

Why don't we ... ?
Richard, Robert and Rebecca are making suggestions for Father's Day.
Choose the first half of each suggestion. Write the letters to find out what Dad would like to do.

Richard

1 .... going to the seaside?
| **p** How about | **h** Why don't we |

2 .... go for a picnic.
| **a** Why don't we | **l** Let's |

3 .... to go to the zoo?
| **s** How about | **a** Would you like |

4 .... going for a walk?
| **m** Why don't we | **y** How about |

5 .... go to the museum?
| **e** Let's | **g** Why don't we |

6 .... play football?
| **n** Let's | **o** Why don't we |

Rebecca

7 .... to go bowling?
| **i** Shall we | **l** Would you like |

8 .... go to the cinema.
| **f** Let's | **t** How about |

Robert

What would Dad like to do?
Complete the sentence.
Tick (✔) the correct picture.

Dad would like to

....

Souvenir Shopping

Here are some souvenirs from seaside towns in Britain.
Read the prices and write the names of the places on the souvenirs.

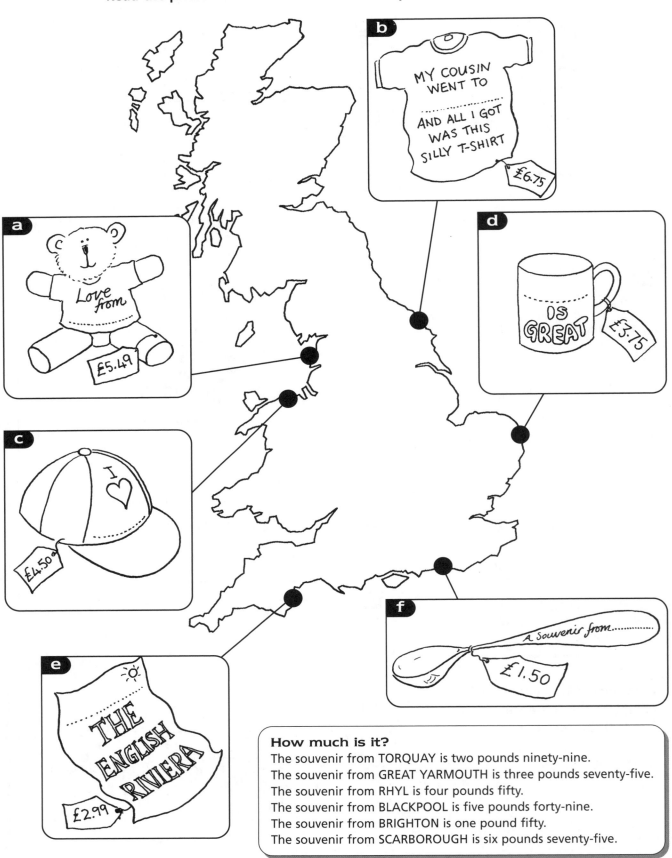

a

Love from

£5.49

b

MY COUSIN WENT TO

....

AND ALL I GOT WAS THIS SILLY T-SHIRT

£6.75

d

IS GREAT

£3.75

c

I ♥

£4.50

e

THE ENGLISH RIVIERA

£2.99

f

A Souvenir from ....

£1.50

How much is it?
The souvenir from TORQUAY is two pounds ninety-nine.
The souvenir from GREAT YARMOUTH is three pounds seventy-five.
The souvenir from RHYL is four pounds fifty.
The souvenir from BLACKPOOL is five pounds forty-nine.
The souvenir from BRIGHTON is one pound fifty.
The souvenir from SCARBOROUGH is six pounds seventy-five.

On Holiday in London

Karen is on holiday in London with her family.
Look at the signs and write the answers to Karen's questions.

Use these answers:

Yes, we can.   No, we can't.   Yes, you can.   No, you can't.

1 Hyde Park

Can I go
in a boat?

2 London Zoo

Can I feed
the animals?

3 River Thames

Can we swim
in the river?

4 Pub

Can I go
in the pub?

5 Madame Tussaud's

Can I take
a photograph?

6 Wimbledon

Can we watch
the tennis?

Holiday Dot to Dot

Join the words and make twelve holiday words. Write the words under the pictures.
Then join the numbers. What is the picture?

post (**1**)	fish (**4**)	ice- (**4**)	guard (**8**)
star (**1**)	board (**5**)	suit (**5**)	site (**8**)
swim (**6**)	ball (**6**)	camp (**7**)	glasses (**5**)
sea (**2**)	card (**2**)	roller (**9**)	case (**10**)
surf (**4**)	weed (**3**)	life (**6**)	cream (**7**)
volley (**2**)	suit (**9**)	sun (**3**)	coaster (**10**)

a

postcard

b

c

d

e

f

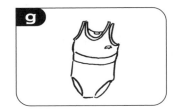

g

h

i

j

k

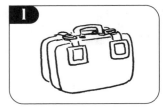

l

```
    1 ————————— 2        3
                          •
  4 •                  • 5


             • 6


   7 •          8     9      • 10
                •     •
```

Lost at the Airport
Read what happened on Mark's holiday last year.
Choose the correct words and write the letters. Find out where Mark's little brother was.

We were going on holiday to Ibiza. We checked in our luggage at the airport and went to look in the shops because we were an hour early. Suddenly we realised that my little brother, Danny, wasn't with us.

1. 'Oh, no,' said my mother. 'I hope **something** a / *nothing* i has happened to him.'

2. 'He must be **somewhere** n / *nowhere* t,' I said.

3. We looked for him in all the shops, but we couldn't find him **everywhere** o / *anywhere* t.

4. An air steward came and asked, 'Is **everything** h / *something* s alright?' So we told him about our problem.

5. He asked all his friends, 'Has **anyone** e / *everyone* g seen a little boy?'

6. But **someone** r / *noone* t had seen him.

7. We looked in the newsagent's and in the chemist's, but Danny was **nowhere** o / *everywhere* u to be seen.

8. I thought I saw Danny in the cafe, but it was **anyone** b / *someone* i else.

9. I called Danny's name but **noone** a / *everyone* l in the cafe stared at me and I was embarrassed.

10. 'We've looked **everywhere** e / *nowhere* p,' said my mum.

11. 'There isn't **something** y / *anything* t else we can do,' said my dad.

Then I had an idea. I went to look for Danny __ __   __ __ __   __ __ __ __ __ __ and I found him. We had to run to catch our plane because we were very late.

Which boy is Danny?

Holiday Puzzle

Work out the code and write the words in the crossword.
Most of the words are connected with **summer holidays**.
Each letter has a number. There are four letters already in the crossword to help you.

C is number 9.
M is number 13.
I is number 15.
G is number 22.

First write all the Cs, Ms, Is and Gs.
Then work out the numbers of all the other letters.

A   N
B   O
~~C~~   P
D   Q
E   R
F   S
~~G~~   T
H   U
~~I~~   V
J   W
K   X
L   Y
~~M~~   Z

20	11		17	20			26	5	17	3	3	15	9 C
11	1	9	15	26	11	2		5		13		12		8
	15		5		26	5	17	15	21		17	21		12
15	26		14			15		14	8	8	6			21
9		24	8		8	21		24			6		15	26
11		26	5	12	21	23	24		21	8		18		5
	4	17	26			12		15		10	12	6	16
24		5		14	15	9	21	15	9			11	
9	17	3	11		24			24	11	17	22	12	6	6
12		15		4		22 G		26	8	11		17
4	17	24	23	11	26	4	17	6	6		21		7
17		19		17		13 M		19	11	17	25	16
	2		9	17	25	11		17			17		17
9	8	17	9	19		24	20	15 I	13	13	15	21	22

1	2	3	4	5	6	7	8	9	10	11	12	13
								C				M

14	15	16	17	18	19	20	21	22	23	24	25	26
	I							G				

Now use the same code to find a popular holiday destination for British tourists.

| 9 | 8 | 24 | 26 | 17 |

| 2 | 11 | 6 |

| 24 | 8 | 6 |

Carnival Wordsearch

Every year in London there is a Caribbean carnival. It is in a part of London called Notting Hill.
Find 22 Carnival words in the wordsearch. Solve the anagrams and write the words.

The words go ➡, ⬇ and ↘.

```
B E C F A M I L I E S
B C H I L D R E N A U
A A O M U S I C F U N
U R N S W S E I P G S
T N I D T E S T R U H
O I O C C U E O I S I
L V D I R R M K Z T N
P A R A D E O E E N E
A L F O O D G W S N F
R D A N C I N G D E D
T R I N I D A D A S B
Y R U G A M E S A E R
N O T T I N G H I L L
Y L O N D O N O I S Y
```

1. drinchle   _children_ ....
2. Agustu   ....
3. sumci   ....
4. gadincn   ....
5. raggee   ....
6. tumessoc   ....
7. racvnali   ....
8. ttiNong liHl ....
9. zseirp   ....
10. Trandidi   ....
11. tarpy   ....
12. odof   ....
13. suneshin   ....
14. abdn   ....
15. rdaepa   ....
16. mseag   ....
17. unf   ....
18. miseifal   ....
19. nodLno   ....
20. eknwede   ....
21. crodws   ....
22. ysoin   ....

In lots of countries Carnival is in February or March. In London Carnival is in August. Why?
Write the letters that are left in the wordsearch grid to find the answer.

_ _

Looking Good

Look at the Carnival picture and choose the correct word in each speech bubble.

9 Don't go to the toilets. They smell **fine** 650 / *disgusting* 450.

6 This music is great. Everyone looks **sunny** 400 / *happy* 230.

10 It's been a long day. I feel **tired** 250 / *sweet* 900.

1 I love your costume. You look **kind** 450 / *beautiful* 200.

8 I don't like this music. It sounds **awful** 110 / *big* 800.

7 I like this band. They sound **brilliant** 150 / *messy* 60.

2 That's a great costume. You look **quiet** 90 / *funny* 160

5 Maria has eaten too much and she feels **greedy** 280 / *sick* 50.

3 Shall we buy some food here? It smells **nice** 100 / *pretty* 200.

4 Would you like some curry? It tastes **delicious** 300 / *comfortable* 750.

How many people go to the Notting Hill Carnival every year?
Add up all the numbers of the correct answers. Multiply the total by 1,000.

.... people go to carnival every year.

Carnival Maze

Beverley is talking about the Carnival.

Read what she says and choose the correct word to complete each phrasal verb.

Choose the correct answers and find something that is always guaranteed at Carnival.

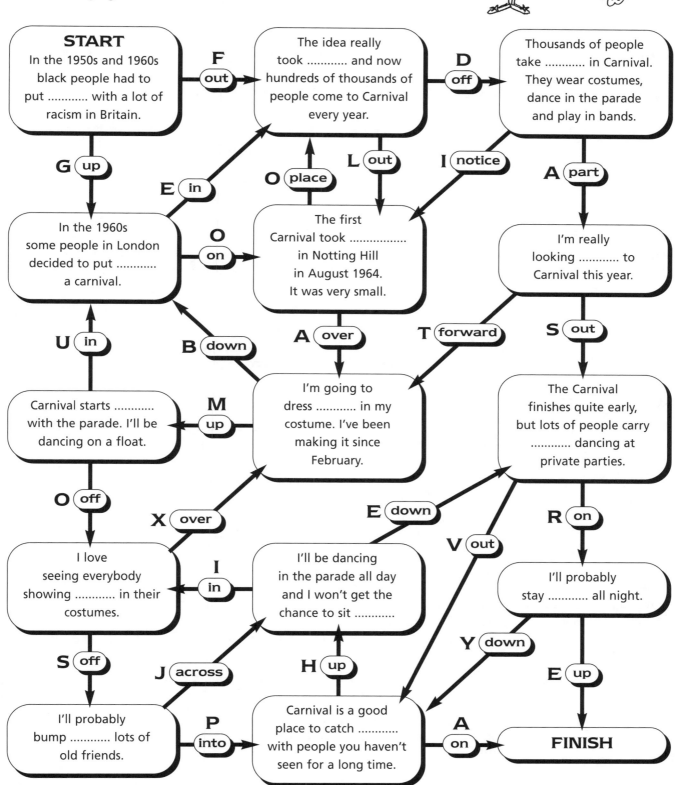

START
In the 1950s and 1960s black people had to put .... with a lot of racism in Britain.

F out

The idea really took .... and now hundreds of thousands of people come to Carnival every year.

D off

Thousands of people take .... in Carnival. They wear costumes, dance in the parade and play in bands.

G up

E in

O place

L out

I notice

A part

In the 1960s some people in London decided to put .... a carnival.

O on

The first Carnival took .... in Notting Hill in August 1964. It was very small.

I'm really looking .... to Carnival this year.

U in

B down

A over

T forward

S out

Carnival starts .... with the parade. I'll be dancing on a float.

M up

I'm going to dress .... in my costume. I've been making it since February.

The Carnival finishes quite early, but lots of people carry .... dancing at private parties.

O off

X over

E down

R on

I love seeing everybody showing .... in their costumes.

I in

I'll be dancing in the parade all day and I won't get the chance to sit ....

V out

I'll probably stay .... all night.

S off

J across

H up

Y down

E up

I'll probably bump .... lots of old friends.

P into

Carnival is a good place to catch .... with people you haven't seen for a long time.

A on

FINISH

Odd One Out

**Find out about the Highland Games. Find the word to complete each sentence.
Write the letters to complete the name of the most famous event in the Highland Games.**

1

The Highland Games are in ....
w England   b London   d Wales   t Scotland

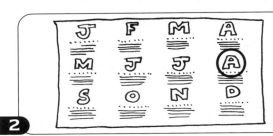

2

The Highland Games are in ....
h August   r January   a Monday   l October

3

Lots of people wear a ....
u dress   o shirt   e kilt   g newspaper

4

There are .... competitions.
c dancing   p sleeping   m acting   i singing

5

There are .... races.
n river   i telephone   v forest   a hill

6

There is a .... throwing competition.
k saw   b hammer   e drill   p frog

7

In the tug-of-war two teams pull a ....
e cake   r shoelace   e rope   f string

8

At the end of the Highland Games there is a big
.... fight.
s book   r pillow   y duvet   t sheet

This competition is called tossing

_ _ _ _ _ _ _ .

**Now find the word that is different
in each line. Write the letters and
find the name of this Scottish
instrument. You can hear it at the
Highland Games.**

_ _ _ _ _ _ _ _

Competitions

The Highland Games take place all over Scotland in August. These are traditional Scottish competitions.

These are some of the competitions.

Complete the sentences and find the words in the wordsearch.

F	A	S	T	E	S	T	H
U	F	A	S	T	L	F	I
R	A	B	E	S	T	A	G
T	R	H	I	G	H	S	H
H	I	G	H	E	S	T	E
E	F	U	R	T	H	E	R
S	B	E	T	T	E	R	S
T	K	I	W	E	L	L	T

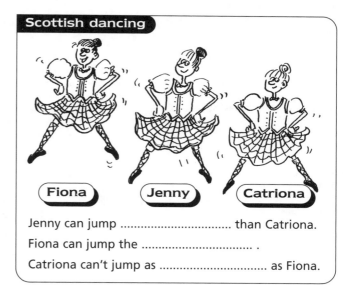

Scottish dancing

Fiona   Jenny   Catriona

Jenny can jump .... than Catriona.

Fiona can jump the ....

Catriona can't jump as .... as Fiona.

Tossing the caber

James's throw

Andrew's throw

Hamish's throw

James can't toss the caber as .... as Hamish.

Andrew can toss the caber .... than James.

Hamish can throw the caber the ....

Hill race

Stuart

Moira

Robert

Robert can run the ....

Stuart can't run as .... as Moira.

Moira can run .... than Stuart.

Bagpipes

Pauline 1st prize   Angus 2nd prize   Donald 3rd prize

Pauline can play the bagpipes .... than Angus.

Donald can't play the bagpipes as .... as Angus.

Pauline can play the bagpipes the ....

pages 6 and 7
Festivals and Special Days
Autumn: September, October, November
Winter: December, January, February
Spring: March, April, May
Summer: June, July, August

January: New Year's Day
February: Valentine's Day
March: St Patrick's Day, St David's Day, Mother's day
April: April Fool's Day, St George's Day
May: May Day
June: Father's Day
July: Summer Holidays
August: Notting Hill Carnival
September: Back to School
October: Hallowe'en
November: St Andrew's Day, Bonfire Night
December: Christmas Day

page 8
Birthday Parties
1. Natasha, **2.** Simon, **3.** Davina, **4.** Rashid, **5.** Louise, **6.** Matthew, **7.** Helen, **8.** Hamish

	p	i	c	n	i	c		
		b	o	w	l	i	n	g
	c	i	n	e	m	a		
t	h	e	m	e	p	a	r	k
r	e	s	t	a	u	r	a	n	t
	s	k	a	t	i	n	g	
	t	h	e	a	t	r	e	
	p	a	r	t	y			

The birthday present is a **computer**.

page 9
Birthday Presents
1. a ring, **2.** a bicycle, **3.** a teddy bear. **4.** a picture, **5.** a calculator, **6.** a T-shirt, **7.** a bag, **8.** a hair dryer, **9.** some books, **10.** a flute

page 10
What's in the Picture?
You can see: **2.** grass, **5.** a dog, **8.** nuts, **9.** a boy, **11.** a mouse, **15.** a fox, **18.** mushrooms, **19.** leaves, **22.** an umbrella, **24.** squirrels, **26.** spiders, **27.** flowers, **30.** trees

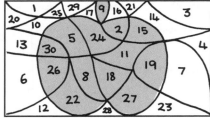

It's an apple.

page 11
Find the Differences
In picture A there are lots of leaves on the tree.
In picture B there are a few leaves on the tree.
In picture A there are lots of/ plenty of birds.
In picture B there are a couple of birds.
In picture A there are a few squirrels.
In picture B there are a couple of squirrels.
In picture A thre are a few cars.
In picture B there are a couple of cars.
In picture A there are lots of/ plenty of mushrooms.
In picture B there are a few mushrooms.
In picture A there are lots of/plenty of flowers.
In picture B there are a few flowers.
In picture A there are lots of/plenty of houses.
In picture B there are a few houses.
In picture A there are a few trees.
In picture B there are a couple of trees.
In picture A there are a few clouds.
In picture B there is one cloud.

page 10
The Back to School Alphabet
A atlas, **B** bag, **C** calculator, **D** dictionary, **E** exercise books, **F** football, **G** gym, **H** homework, **I** infants, **J** jacket, **K** kids, **L** lunch, **M** magazine, **N** notebook, **O** overhead projector, **P** pens and pencils, **Q** questions, **R** ruler, **S** sports kit, **T** teacher, **U** uniform, **V** violin, **W** watch, **X** xylophone, **Y** yawn, **Z** zero

page 13
Going Back to School

	Year	Name of teacher	Transport
Shona	Year 7	Ms Moore	van
Natalie	Sixth form	Mr Raman	train
Daniel	Year 11	Ms Martinez	walking
Nathan	Year 9	Mrs Peel	bike
Raminder	Year 8	Mr Bryant	bus
James	Year 10	Mr Turton	car

1. Natalie, **2.** Shona, **3.** Daniel, **4.** James, **5.** Nathan, **6.** Raminder.

page 14
GCSE options
There are several possible answers involving personal response to this puzzle.

page 15
Fruit and Vegetables
It's a **corn dolly**.

page 16
Harvest Boxes
2. Mrs Brown, **3.** Mr Clare, **4.** Mrs Gower, **5.** Mrs Watts, **6.** Mr Flint, **7.** Mr Short
Box number **1** is for **Mrs Blake**.

page 17
Rosh Hashanah Traditions
1. clean, **2.** give, **3.** go, **4.** ask, **5.** eat, **6.** say
The musical instrument is a **shofar**.

page 18
Bad Things

page 19
What Time Is It?
1. eleven o'clock, **2.** half past five, **3.** quarter to three, **4.** quarter past six, **5.** ten to seven, **6.** ten past ten, **7.** twenty-five past twelve, **8.** twenty to two, **9.** five past eight, **10.** twenty to one, **11.** five to four, **12.** twenty-five to nine

page 20
An Hour Ahead
1. True. **2.** False. At five o'clock David will have dinner. **3.** False. At twelve o'clock David will have lunch. **4.** True. **5.** False. At ten o'clock in the morning David will play football. **6.** False. At four o'clock David will play computer games. **7.** False. At seven o'clock David will watch TV. **8.** False. At three o'clock David will ride his bike. **9.** True. **10.** False. At eleven o'clock David will wash his mum's car.

page 21
Hallowe'en Costumes
witch: 1. hat, 2. dress, 3. coat, 4. shoes
vampire: 5. shirt, 6. cloak, 7. trousers
cat: 8. mask, 9. jumper, 10. gloves, 11. leggings, 12. slippers

1 →	g	d	h	j	o	l	s	t
	t	r	o	u	s	e	r	s
	d	e	f	m	c	g	a	l
2 →	b	s	a	p	o	g	t	i
	l	s	x	e	a	i	y	p
	s	h	i	r	t	n	q	p
3 →	a	l	i	e	n	g	m	e
	g	l	o	v	e	s	a	r
	s	h	o	e	s	h	s	s
	u	z	c	l	o	a	k	w
4 →	m	o	n	s	t	e	r	

1) ghost, **2)** bat, **3)** alien, **4)** monster

page 22
Hallowe'en Apples

girl's name	boy's name
Deborah	Daniel
Sarah	Stephen
Paula	Peter
Alice	Andrew
Tina	Tony
Juliet	Jeremy
Michelle	Mark
Rachel	Richard
Caroline	Christopher

page 23
Are You Superstitious?
Mostly ▲ :
You are not superstitious. You are a very practical person. You only believe what you can see and you believe that you make your own luck. For you, Hallowe'en is a time to have fun and go to parties.

Mostly 😺 :
You are very superstitious. You believe in ghosts and in good and bad luck. For you, Hallowe'en is a time for spells and magic. It's scary but it's exciting, too.

Equal ▲ and 😺 :
You are sometimes superstitious. You would like to believe in magic, but you are also realistic. At Hallowe'en you like to try the superstitions and see if they come true.

page 24
Who's the Thief?
It can't have been Hannah because she must be the witch.
It can't have been Kerry because she must be the cat.
It can't have been Darren because he must be the pumpkin.
It can't have been Vicky because she must be the ghost.
It can't have been Steve because he must be Frankenstein.
It can't have been Naima because she must be the alien.
It must have been Chris because he must be Dracula.

page 23
Guys
A. This is Marcus's guy. B. This is Sam's guy.
C. This is Paul's guy. D. This is Gloria's guy

page 26
Where Are the Pets?
(answers to come once the a/w is in)
1. Joey, 2. Sam, 3. Bubbles, 4. Ben,
5. Jaguar, 6. Morgan, 7. Snowy, 8. Tiger,
9. Sandy, 10. Captain, 11. Waffles,
12. Toby.

page 27
Bonfire Night Safety
1. Don't throw fireworks.
2. Keep your fireworks in a metal box.
3. Don't put fireworks near the bonfire.
4. Don't light fireworks in the house.
5. Don't light fireworks with a match.
6. Light fireworks with a taper.
7. Keep your pets in the house.
8. Don't cook food on the bonfire.
9. Wear warm clothes.

Draw a cross on pictures 1, 3, 4, 5 and 8.

page 28
The Story of Guy Fawkes
1. No it isn't. It's a story from the seventeenth century. (R) 2. No, they weren't. They were Catholics. (O) 3. Yes, there were. (B) 4. Yes, there was. (E) 5. Yes, they did. (R) 6. Yes, he did. (T) 7. No, it wasn't. It was the 5th of November 1605. (C) 8. No, it didn't. The king's soldiers discovered the plan. (A) 9. No, he didn't. He decided to kill Guy Fawkes and his friends. (T) 10. Yes, they do. (E) 11. No, they don't. They make models of Guy Fawkes. (S) 12. Yes, they are. (B) 13. No, they aren't. Toffee apples, soup and baked potatoes are popular. (Y)

The leader of the Gunpowder Plot was called **Robert Catesby**.

page 29
Toffee Apples
You will need: **450 grams** soft brown sugar, **350 grams** butter, **5 millilitres** vinegar, **150 millilitres** water, **10** apples, **10** wooden skewers
1. Lightly, 2. slowly, occasionally, 3. rapidly, 4. immediately, 5. Carefully, 7. neatly

page 30
Preparing for Diwali
1. Anita: Sheetal's auntie, Sanjay: Sheetal's little brother 2. Anand: Sheetal's uncle 3. Rahim: Sheetal's little cousin 4. Tara: Sheetal's little sister 5. Deepa: Sheetal's older cousin 6. Nilesh: Sheetal's big brother 7. Geeta: Sheetal's big sister 8. Ranjit: Sheetal's dad, Priya: Sheetal's mum

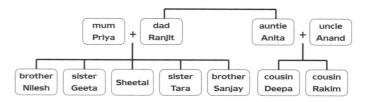

page 31
Rama and Sita
1. who, 2. who, 3. that, 4. where, 5. where, 6. who, 7. that, 8. that, 9. who, 10. where, 11. who

page 32
Winter Weather
1. freezing (It's raining.) 2. windy (It's cloudy.) 3. cloudy (It's sunny.) 4. sunny (It's snowing.) 5. foggy (It's cold.) 6. raining (It's freezing.) 7. cold (It's foggy.) 8. snowing (It's windy.)

page 33
Who Likes Winter?
1. No, she doesn't. 2. Yes, she is. 3. No, he wouldn't. 4. No, he won't. 5. Yes, he can. 6. Yes, he has. 7. Yes, she will. 8. Yes, she has. 9. Yes, she can. 10. Yes, she would. 11. No, he isn't. 12. No, he doesn't. Does Eleanor like the winter? *No, she doesn't.* Does Ian like the winter? *No, he doesn't.* Does Mike like the winter? *Yes, he does.* Does Catherine like the winter? *Yes, she does.* Does Angela like the winter? *Yes, she does.* Does Paul like the winter? *No, he doesn't.*

page 34
Advent Calendar
twenty-one: Christmas card, sixteen: shepherd, seven: donkey, eleven: candle, twenty-four: angel, three: Father Christmas, thirteen: turkey, eight: snowflake, nineteen: Christmas tree, six: bell, fourteen: snowman, one: holly, twenty-five: baby Jesus, seventeen: reindeer, ten: kings, twenty-two: present, five: Christmas cake, four: hat, eighteen: star, twelve: robin, nine: bauble, twenty-three: Christmas pudding, two: cracker, fifteen: sleigh, twenty: stocking.

page 35
Christmas Show
1. Martine is **acting** in the Nativity **play**.
2. Alistair is **playing** the **trumpet**.
3. Rebecca is **pulling** the **curtains**.

4. Ranjeet is **painting** the **scenery**.
5. Anna is **playing** the **drums**.
6. Liam is **reading** a **poem**.
7. Adelle is **singing** a **carol**.
8. Paul is **helping** with the **lights**.
9. Danielle is **giving** presents to the **children**.
10. Richard is **selling** the **tickets**.
11. Emma is **making** the **costumes**.
12. Oliver is **making** the **masks**.

Jonathan is C: Father Christmas

pages 36 and 37
Giant Christmas Crossword

```
M E R R Y C H R I S T M A S
I     R   A     I     A N T
N O   S T A M P   N   K   A
C   E   N   C     U G L I E R
E   D O N K E Y   E     N   R
P   W   E   E   R       G E T
I V Y     R U L E S       I
E   E   L   L A   E W A N
S A N T A   S O R R Y     S
    L   C R O W N   E   W E
F L A M E   I   L   O I L
    M I S T L E T O E   D
O   S   E       G A M E S
P R E S E N T S   S T I R
U       U       N     N O
D A Y   B A R K   W A T C H
I       H E   M E N     A
S       L   E V E     O N
N   H O L L Y   C A R D S
G   E     I   I   U   L
    W R A P P I N G P A P E R
```

page 38
A Christmas Carol
The Ghost of Christmas Past: 2, 8, 10, 12
The Ghost of Christmas Present: 1, 5, 6, 11
The Ghost of Christmas Future: 3, 4, 7, 9
What happens next? b) Scrooge will become kinder and pay Bob Cratchit more money.

page 39
New Year in Scotland
1. whisky, 2. fireworks, 3. bagpipes,
4. champagne, 5. coal, 6. Edinburgh,

7. dance, 8. party The Scottish word for New Year is **Hogmanay**.

page 40
New Year's Resolutions
1g, 2h, 3e, 4f, 5d, 6a, 7j, 8c, 9b, 10i

page 41
Celebrating the New Year
1. celebrated, 2. led, 3. played, 4. invented, 5. moved, 6. sent, 7. worn, 8. burned, 9. celebrated, 10. held, 11. eaten, 12. baked, 13. cleaned, 14. bought, 15. sung, 16. visited, 17. made, 18. given, 19. lit, 20. floated, 21. told, 22. performed, 23. frightened, 24. worn

```
S H A H L I T F E L E D
E F C E L E B R A T E D
N L E L V I S I T E D P
T O L D P P Y G E N I E
P A E W O R N H N B N R
L T B O U G H T E A V F
A E R R G I V E N K E O
Y D A N W S U N G E N R
E Y T B U R N E D D T M
D E E M O V E D A R E E
M A D E C L E A N E D D
```

The message is: Happy New Year.

page 42
The Muslim Year

Month	Number
Ramadan	*ninth month*
Dhul-Qa'dah	*eleventh month*
Jumada-l-Ula	*fifth month*
Rajab	*seventh month*
Dhul-Hijjah	*twelfth month*
Muharram	*first month*
Rabi ath-Thani	*fourth month*
Jumada-th-Thaniyyah	*sixth month*
Shawwal	*tenth month*
Rabi al-Awwal	*third month*
Safar	*second month*
Sha'ban	*eighth month*

page 43
Fast and Festival
12. During, 16. during, 22. until, 4. At, 18. first, 7. later, 2. before, 20. While, 3. during, 13. during, 6. until, 5. while, 19. while, 1. when, 23. While, 8. at, 10. on, 17. Before, 9. On, 15. before, 24. often, 14. until, 21. When, 11. At

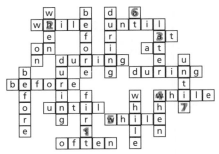

The month after Ramadan is called **Shawwal**.

page 44
Animal Years
rat: happy, sociable
ox: patient, shy
tiger: confident, bossy
rabbit: peaceful, shy
dragon: generous, moody
snake: funny, selfish
horse: ambitious, careful
ram: artistic, kind
monkey: cheeky, clever
rooster: organised, faithful
dog: brave, loving
pig: strong, honest

page 45
Code Breaker

20	7	13
b	a	d

18	19	16
c	u	t

9	2	13
r	e	d

12	5	5	13
g	o	o	d

8	2	7	9
y	e	a	r

18	5	17	13
c	o	l	d

13	2	7	16	4
d	e	a	t	h

4	7	6	6	8
h	a	p	p	y

14	11	10	15	2
k	n	i	f	e

3	5	11	2	8
m	o	n	e	y

9	7	10	11	1
r	a	i	n	s

1	11	5	21	1
s	n	o	w	s

a) rains, b) snows, c) cold, d) good, e) year, f) knife, g) cut, h) bad, i) death, j) happy, k) money, l) red

9	10	18	2
r	i	c	e

17	10	5	11
l	i	o	n

13	9	19	3
d	r	u	m

18	7	9	13	1
c	a	r	d	s

13	9	7	12	5	11
d	r	a	g	o	n

6	5	1	16	2	9
p	o	s	t	e	r

20	19	13	13	4	7
B	u	d	d	h	a

17	7	11	16	2	9	11
l	a	n	t	e	r	n

13	19	3	6	17	10	11	12	1
d	u	m	p	l	i	n	g	s

15	10	9	2	18	9	7	18	14	2	9	1
f	i	r	e	c	r	a	c	k	e	r	s

1. dragon, 2. rice, 3. cards, 4. firecrackers,
5. Buddha, 6. dumplings, 7. poster, 8. lion,
9. drum, 10. lantern

page 46
Burns Night Quiz
one Scottish
six 25 January 1759
nineteen He is a famous poet.
eight in the evening
fourteen a pudding made of meat, oats
and spices
eleven potatoes and turnips
seventeen the bagpipes
nine a kilt
sixteen a ceilidh

page 47
Poem
1. melody, 2. played, 3. you are so
beautiful, 4. pretty, 5. girl, 6. you, 7. all,
8. go, 9. with, 10. of, 11. goodbye,
12. for a short time, 13. though
First verse: picture B
Second verse: picture D
Third verse: picture C
Fourth verse: picture A

page 48
Valentine's Cards
1. cheeky, 2. mean, 3. fair, 4. sweet, 5. busy,
6. bright, 7. great, 8. funny, 9. clever
Roses are **red**
Violets are **blue**
Sugar is **sweet**
And so are **you**

page 49
Computer Dating
Anna Walters

Neither **Darren** nor **Ben** is suitable for
you. Your ideal partner is **Curtis**.
Ben Taylor
Either **Gemma** or **Vicky** is suitable for you.
Your ideal partner is **Gemma**.
Amy Callaghan
Neither **Ben** nor **Nick** is suitable for you.
Your ideal partner is **Darren**.
Nick Short
Neither **Amy** nor **Gemma** is suitable for
you. Your ideal partner is **Vicky**.
Gemma Theakston
Either **Ben** or **Darren** is suitable for you.
Your ideal partner is **Ben**.
Curtis Jackson
Either **Anna** or **Amy** is suitable for you.
Your ideal partner is **Anna**.
Vicky Bradshaw
Neither **Curtis** nor **Darren** is suitable for
you. Your ideal partner is **Nick**.
Darren Wallis
Either **Amy** or **Gemma** is suitable for you.
Your ideal partner is **Amy**.

page 50
The Story of Valentine's Day
1. February, 2. Juno, 3. women, 4. husband,
5. times, 6. wall, 7. loved, 8. festival,
9. poems, 10. men, 11. post, 12. cards,
13. on, 14. teddy

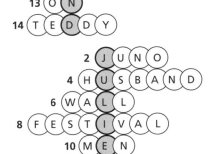

page 51
Pancake Fillings
5 c h e e s e
1 h a m
3 s t r a w b e r r i e s
4 o n i o n
2 a v o c a d o
1 e g g s
8 c h o c o l a t e
3 n u t s

6 i c e - c r e a m
1 s p i n a c h
6 s m o k e d s a l m o n
4 b a n a n a s
5 h o n e y

Shrove Tuesday

page 52
Pancake Tossing Competition
Kieran tosses 17 pancakes.
Holly tosses 16 pancakes.
Martin tosses 22 pancakes.
Jason tosses 20 pancakes.
Tiffany tosses 18 pancakes.
Martin tosses the most pancakes.

page 53
Lent
1. buying clothes 2. swimming 3. going to
the theatre 4. eating cake 5. eating
sweets 6. singing 7. going to the cinema
8. acting 9. going to school 10. listening
to music 11. cycling.
Number 9 is joking.

page 54
Animal Photographs

	adult	babies
1	deer	fawn
2	rabbit	baby rabbits
3	bird	chicks
4	fox	fox cubs
5	mouse	baby mice
6	badger	badger cubs
7	frog	tadpoles
8	otter	otter cub
9	duck	ducklings
10	cow	calf
11	sheep	lambs
12	horse	foal

page 55
Spring Festivals
1d, 2b, 3f, 4a, 5g, 6h, 7e, 8c
1. Easter, 2. Mother's Day, 3. April Fool's
Day, 4. May Day, 5. St Patrick's Day,
6. Comic Relief, 7. Palm Sunday,
8. St David's Day

page 56
Saints' Names
The patron saint of Scotland is St Andrew.
The patron saint of Wales is St David. The
patron saint of England is St George. The
patron saint of Ireland is St Patrick.

page 57
St Patrick's Day Postcard
1. found, 2. listened, 3. been, 4. eaten,
5. watched, 6. bought. The Irish word for
festival is *fleadh*.

page 58
Welsh and English
CAERDYDD

1	M	A	R	C	H		
2		W	A	L	E	S	
3			R	U	G	B	Y
4		D	A	V	I	D	
5	E	I	G	H	T	Y	
6		F	E	S	T	I	V	A	L
7	D	A	F	F	O	D	I	L

ABERTAWE

8		S	H	E	E	P	
9	S	N	O	W	D	O	N
10	D	R	A	G	O	N	
11	S	I	N	G	I	N	G
12	C	A	S	T	L	E	
13	C	H	E	E	S	E	
14	R	A	I	N			

CAERDYDD → CARDIFF
ABERTAWE ← SWANSEA

page 59
Making Words
1. house, 2. Monday, 3. dog, 4. hand,
5. man, 6. sun, 7. sum/maths, 8. shoe,
9. orange, 10. north, 11. Thursday,
12. radio, 13. ring, 14. rain, 15. ear,
16. nuts, 17. tongue, 18. mug, 19. mouse,
20. ghost, 21. south, 22. nose, 23. shirt, 24.
horse, 25. Saturday, 26. rose,
27. mouth, 28. hen, 29. monster, 30. heart

pages 60 and 61
Mother's Day Traditions

A: a) May, b) presents, c) girls, d) from,
e) went, f) maids, g) hard, h) not, i) very,
j) off, k) but, l) holiday, m) home, n) visit,

o) used, p) mixture, q) sugar, r) marzipan

B: a) My, b) am, c) first, d) age, e) eleven,
f) mother, g) had, h) up, i) on, j) hat,
k) ate, l) at, m) out, n) journey, o) so,
p) walk, q) quickly, r) lots, s) cake, t) look,
u) flowers

| 5 | 2 | 9 | 20 | 15 | 4 | | 13 | 10 | 14 | 15 |
| s | i | m | n | e | l | | c | a | k | e |

page 62
What Colour Is It?
a) blue, b) pink, c) brown, d) grey,
e) black, f) yellow, g) purple, h) green,
i) white. **Red** is left.
1. ears, 2. hair, 3. glasses, 4. trousers,
5. gloves, 6. teeth, 7. moustache, 8. tie,
9. shoes. **Nose** is left.
People wear a **red nose** for Comic Relief.

page 63
New School Rules
3, 4, 8, 10, 12, 13, 17 and 18 are Red Nose
Day rules. The picture is b) **a face**.

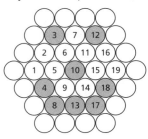

page 64
Charity Projects
1. up, 2. off, 3. up, 4. over, 5. into,
6. through, 7. out, on, 8. out, 9. away

page 65
Who Is the fool?
1. It's nine o'clock. Esther. 2. It's half past
eleven. Jason. 3. It's half past one. Simon.
4. It's half past nine. Anna. 5. It's eleven
o'clock. Miss O'Donnell. 6. It's one o'clock.
Edward. 7. It's half past twelve. Sonia.
8. It's ten o'clock. Joseph.

Page 66
Are You an April Fool?
1. wanted, 2. was ringing, 3. was
snowing, 4. was crawling, 5. was, 6. had
bought, 7. had broken
Mostly a You love playing tricks. You are
funny and you are like making your
friends laugh. Sometimes you go too far.
Remember that not everybody likes it
when you you play tricks on them!
Mostly b You are cool and sophisticated.
Your image is very important to you and
you prefer intelligent conversation to
playing tricks. Remember that it's
important to have a sense of humour, too!
Mostly c You are sensitive and kind. You

don't like to hurt people's feelings. You
get upset when people play tricks on you.
Try not to take it too seriously. Tricks are
usually just fun, not nasty.

page 67
Easter Egg Hunt
1. 7D, 2. 2D, 3. 8J, 4. 8F, 5. 3K, 6. 1I, 7. 5I,
8. 5E

page 68
Hot Cross Buns
a) melt, b) knead, c) beat, d) pour, e) stir,
f) divide, g) add, h) put, i) sift, j) cover,
k) cut, l) place.
1d, 2g, 3i, 4a, 5c, 6e, 7b, 8f, 9l, 10j, 11k,
12h

page 69
Easter Words
1. PALM, PALE, MALE, MOLE, HOLE, HOLY
2. HOLY, HOLD, COLD, TOLD, GOLD,
GOOD
3. EASTER, SISTER, FASTER, FITTER,
HOTTER, MATTER, MADDER, HARDER,
HANDEL, SANDAL, SUNDAY
4. BUNS, BANS, BAND, HAND, HARD,
HARE

page 70
Maypole Dancing
1. She is tall and she has got glasses.
(Kirsten)
2. He is quite short. (Ben)
3. She has got very long straight hair.
(Andrea)
4. She has got straight hair and glasses.
(Imogen)
5. He is tall and quite fat. (Damon)
6. She has got short curly hair. (Alice)
7. He is tall and thin. (Nick)
8. He has got curly blond hair. (Harry)
9. He has got straight dark hair. (Yusef)
10. He has got round glasses. (Liam)
11. She has got straight dark hair. (Odile)

1) Ben, 2) Alice, 3) Nick, 4) Kirsten,
5) Harry, 6) Odile, 7) Liam, 8) Imogen,
9) Damon, 10) Andrea, 11) Yusef
Bank Holiday is another name for May
Day.

page 71
Word Spirals
A

5 E	A	S	6 Y	O	U	7 R
C	12 L	E	A	13 S	T	U
I	B	16 E	S	T	O	L
4 M	11 A	Y	P	O	L	8 E
R	15 F	E	V	A	14 D	A
A	O	10 S	Y	A	S	9 R
3 W	E	R	2 D	L	O	1 S	←

B

	¹G	R	²E	W	I	N	G	⁴G
	V	⁹E	A	¹⁰T	S	E	O	O
	A	¹⁴M	I	¹⁵S	S	E	L	
⁸G	A	R	L	A	¹¹N	⁴D		
N	X	I	¹⁶G	N	E	O		
O	¹³E	V	¹²I	D	E	O		
⁷L	L	⁶E	F	O	O	⁵R		

page 72
Theme Park Maze
First ride: big wheel
Second ride: rollercoaster
Third ride: water splash
Fourth ride: dodgems
Fifth ride: space rocket

page 73
Rollercoaster
1. been, 2. nothing, 3. good, 4. drinks,
5. sick, 6. kids, 7. scared, 8. did, 9. didn't,
10. tried, 11. dare, 12. evening, 13. ghost,
14. train, 15. never, 16. rides, 17. surprised,
18. dream, 19. music, 20. couldn't,
21. throw, 22. wouldn't, 23. though,
24. had. 25. dark, 26. know, 27. won

page 74
Which Event?
Christine chooses the javelin. Neelam
chooses the 100 metres. Gemma chooses
the long jump. Melanie chooses the 800
metres. Bryony chooses the high jump

page 75
Who's the Winner?
1. Kate is
B I G – H E A D E D

2. Jake is
B A D – T E M P E R E D

3. Lucy is
K I N D – H E A R T E D

4. Adam is
G O O D – H U M O U R E D

5. Beth is
H A R D – W O R K I N G

6. Mark is
M E A N – S P I R I T E D

7. Arti is
F U N – L O V I N G

8. Zach is
S H O R T – S I G H T E D

Beth wins.

page 76
Tombola
a) some perfume, b) a game, c) nothing, d)
a teddy bear, e) some wine, f) a doll,
g) nothing, h) some candles, i) a Walkman
The CD is left. It is number eight hundred
and sixty-nine.

page 77
Prize Puzzle

	T	o	m		h	a	s		w	o	n
a		t	e	d	d	y.		N	i	c	k
h	a	s		w	o	n		s	o	m	e
	s	w	e	e	t	s.		J	o	h	n
	h	a	s		w	o	n		a	n	
	o	w	l.		B	e	n		h	a	s
	w	o	n		a		d	u	c	k.	
R	i	c	k		h	a	s		w	o	n
	a	n		e	l	e	p	h	a	n	t.

1. Ben, 2. Tom, 3. John, 4. Nick, 5. Rick

page 78
Father's Day Cards
Kerry's dad: I like gardening.
Nick's dad: I like playing golf.
Ruth's dad: I like swimming.
Ewan's dad: I like playing football.
Terri's dad: I like cooking.
Greg's dad: I like dancing.

1f, 2e, 3d, 4c, 5b, 6a

page 79
Why Don't We ... ?
Richard: 1. How about, 2. Let's, 3. Would
you like
Rebecca: 4. How about, 5. Why don't we,
6. Why don't we
Robert: 7. Would you like, 8. Let's

b) Dad would like to play golf.

page 80
Souvenir Shopping
a) Blackpool, b) Scarborough, c) Rhyl,
d) Great Yarmouth, e) Torquay,
f) Brighton.

page 81
On Holiday in London
1. Yes, you can.
2. No, you can't.
3. No, we can't.
4. No, you can't.
5. No, you can't.
6. Yes, we can.

page 82
Holiday Dot to Dot

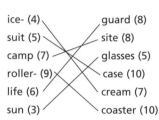

post (1) — fish (4)
star (1) — board (5)
swim (6) — ball (6)
sea (2) — card (2)
surf (4) — weed (3)
volley (2) — suit (9)

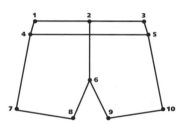

ice- (4) — guard (8)
suit (5) — site (8)
camp (7) — glasses (5)
roller- (9) — case (10)
life (6) — cream (7)
sun (3) — coaster (10)

a) postcard, b) lifeguard, c) campsite,
d) rollercoaster, e) starfish, f) surfboard, g)
swimsuit, h) volleyball, i) ice-cream,
j) sunglasses, k) seaweed, l) suitcase.

It's a pair of shorts.

page 83
Lost at the Airport
1. nothing
2. somewhere
3. anywhere
4. everything
5. anyone
6. noone
7. nowhere
8. someone
9. everyone
10. everywhere
11. anything

in the toilet

Danny is in picture b.

page 84
Holiday Puzzle

The holiday destination is: **Costa Del Sol**

page 85
Carnival Wordsearch

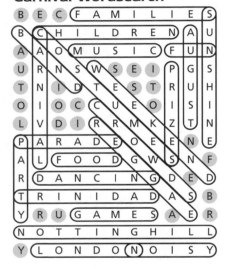

1. children, **2.** August, **3.** music, **4.** dancing,
5. reggae, **6.** costumes, **7.** carnival,
8. Notting Hill, **9.** prizes, **10.** Trinidad,
11. party, **12.** food, **13.** sunshine,
14. band, **15.** parade, **16.** games, **17.** fun,
18. families, **19.** London, **20.** weekend,
21. crowds, **22.** noisy

Because it is too cold in February.

page 86
Looking Good
1. beautiful, **2.** funny, **3.** nice, **4.** delicious,
5. sick. **6.** happy, **7.** brilliant, **8.** big,
9. disgusting, **10.** tired

200 + 160 + 100 + 300 + 50 + 230 + 150 +
110 + 450 + 250 = 2,000

2,000 x 1,000 = 2,000,000

Two million people go to carnival every
year.

page 87
Carnival Maze
In the 1950s and 1960s black people had
to put **up** with a lot of racism in Britain.

In the 1960s some people in London
decided to put **on** a carnival.

The first Carnival took **place** in Notting
Hill in August 1964. It was very small.

The idea really took **off** and now
hundreds of thousands of people come to
Carnival every year.

Thousands of people take **part** in
Carnival. They wear costumes, dance in
the parade and play in bands.

I'm really looking **forward** to Carnival this
year.

I'm going to dress **up** in my costume. I've
been making it since February.

Carnival starts **off** with the parade. I'll be
dancing on a float.

I love seeing everybody showing **off** in
their costumes.

I'll probably bump **into** lots of old friends.

Carnival is a good place to catch **up** with
people yo haven't seen for a long time.

I'll be dancing in the parade all day and I
won't get the chance to sit **down**.

The Carnival finishes quite early, but lots
of people carry **on** dancing at private
parties.

I'll probably stay **up** all night.

GOOD ATMOSPHERE

page 88
Odd One Out
1. Scotland, **2.** August, **3.** kilt, **4.** dancing,
5. hill, **6.** hammer, **7.** rope, **8.** pillow

This competition is called tossing **the
caber**.

The words that are different are:
1. London (London is a town. All the
other words are countries.)

2. Monday (All the others are months.)

3. newspaper (All the others are clothes.)

4. sleeping (All the others are performing
arts.)

5. telephone (All the others are natural
features.)

6. frog (All the others are woodwork
tools.)

7. cake (All the others are things you can
tie.)

8. book (All the others are bed clothes.)

bagpipes

page 89
Competitions
Scottish dancing
Jenny can jump **higher** than Catriona.
Fiona can jump the **highest**.
Catriona can't jump as **high** as Fiona.

Tossing the caber
James can't toss the caber as **far** as
Hamish.
Andrew can toss the caber **further** than
James.
Hamish can throw the caber the **furthest**.

Hill race
Robert can run the **fastest**.
Stuart can't run as **fast** as Moira.
Moira can run **faster** than Stuart.

Bagpipes
Pauline can play the bagpipes **better** than
Angus.
Donald can't play the bagpipes as **well** as
Angus.
Pauline can play the bagpipes the **best**.